De drie stenen

We-hebben-allemaal-wat-boekjes

Jeanette Molema

De drie stenen

Tekeningen:
Wendelien van de Erve

COLUMBUS

De drie stenen
Jeanette Molema

ISBN 978-90-8543-088-9
NUR 282
AVI-4

Illustraties: Wendelien van de Erve
Boekverzorging: Buitenspel, Meppel

Uitgeverij Columbus is onderdeel van
Uitgeversgroep Jongbloed te Heerenveen

www.jongbloed.com

Inhoud

1 · De kast

'Hup Lotte', roept juf.
'Je kunt het best!'
Groep vier heeft gym.
Lotte staat vooraan in de rij.
Ze moet over de kast springen.
Maar ze durft niet.
De kast is veel te hoog!
Riko staat achter Lotte.
Hij duwt Lotte tegen haar rug.
'Kom op, nijlpaard', fluistert Riko.
'Anders ga ik.'
Lotte neemt een aanloop.
Ze zet af en ... beng! Au!
Ze klapt tegen de kast.
Dan glijdt ze weer terug.
Met haar knieën op de harde plank.
Langzaam staat Lotte op.
Ze kijkt om zich heen.
Dik en Rens hangen aan de ringen.
Miek is hoog in het wandrek.
Ze kijkt omlaag naar Lotte.
Ze houdt zich vast met een hand.
De andere hand zwaait naar Lotte.
Lotte hinkt naar de kant.

Juf Ank komt naar haar toe.
'Doet het erg zeer?' vraagt ze.
Lotte knikt.

Ze gaat op de bank zitten.
Juf Ank gaat naast haar zitten.
Het groepje bij de kast springt door.
Hop, hop, hop, hop.
Achter elkaar.
Het lijkt of ze zweven.
'Hoe kon dat nou?' vraagt juf Ank.
'Zo hoog is die kast toch niet?'
Lotte haalt haar schouders op.
'Ik haat gym', zegt ze.
'Wat vind je moeilijk?' vraagt juf Ank.
Ze slaat een arm om Lotte heen.
'Alles', zegt Lotte boos.
'De ringen, een balspel.
De kast, de touwen, alles.'
Juf Ank staat op.
'Blijf maar zitten, het is tijd', zegt ze.
Even later klinkt de fluit.
'Aankleden', roept juf Ank.
Lotte gaat naar de bank in de kleedkamer.
Ze doet haar gymbroek uit.
Op haar knie ziet ze een rode plek.
'Jij viel lelijk', zegt Miek.
Ze loopt naar Lotte toe.
Miek legt haar hand op de plek.
'Ik zag dat je viel', zegt Miek.
'Ik zat hoog in het wandrek.'
Lotte voelt tranen in haar ogen.

Dat komt door Miek.
Ze doet zo aardig.
Miek kan goed gymmen.
Ze vangt de bal altijd.
Ze springt het hoogste van de klas.
Anna komt er ook bij staan.
'Jij bent te dik', zegt ze.
'Daarom kon je niet over de kast.
Je weegt veel te veel.'
Lotte buigt haar hoofd.

Anna praat door.
'Je hebt nooit fruit bij je.
Altijd koek, dat is dom.
Daar word je dik van.'
'Ik lust geen fruit', zegt Lotte.
'Fruit is vies.'
Lotte pakt haar broek.
Ze gaat staan en hijst de broek op.
Anna kijkt naar de broek van Lotte.
Die kan bijna niet dicht.
Lotte houdt haar buik in.
Dan krijgt ze de rits dicht.
'Op een dag krak je door je stoel.
Of je knapt uit je broek', zegt Anna.
'Of je past niet meer door de deur.'
'Hou je mond, tante treuzel', zegt Miek.
'Waar bemoei jij je mee?'
Miek kijkt Lotte aan.
'Kleed je nou maar snel aan', zegt ze.
'We lopen samen naar het plein.'
Dat is fijn, denkt Lotte.
Samen lopen Miek en Lotte naar buiten.
Groep vijf komt eraan lopen.
Zij hebben nu gym.
Hun meester loopt achteraan.
'Wij hebben het gehad', lacht Lotte.
'Daar ben ik blij om.'
Miek kijkt verbaasd.

'Ik vind gym super', zegt ze.
'Straks hebben we sommen, bah!'
'Ik heb er zin in', lacht Lotte.
'We hebben zo de wedstrijd van Sneltel.
Wie doet de sommen het snelst?
Die wordt de nummer een.
Ik hoop dat ik het ben.
Maar Dik is ook zo goed.'
Miek kijkt verbaasd naar Lotte.
'Ik haat Sneltel.
Ik krijg er hoofdpijn van.'
'Echt hoofdpijn?' vraagt Lotte.
'Grapje', lacht Miek.
'Kom op, loop door.
Dan is er nog tijd om te spelen.
Voor je het weet hebben we Sneltel.
Dan word jij vast de winnaar.'

2 · De wedstrijd

Lotte zit er klaar voor.
Ze heeft pen en papier voor zich.
Juf houdt een grote kaart in de lucht.
Er staan zes apen op.
'Deze kaart is voor de winnaar.'
'De winnaar is zo slim als een aap', roept Miek.
'Miek', zegt juf streng.
'Houd toch eens je mond.'
Het is even stil.
'Klaar?' vraagt juf.
'Daar gaat ie dan: 8x5+2.'
Makkie, 42, denkt Lotte.
Ze hoeft daar niet over na te denken.
7x9+18=81.
Ze schrijft het zo op.
Lotte kijkt om zich heen.
Ze ziet Miek op haar pen kauwen.
36-35+19.
Lotte schrijft 20 op.
Ze kijkt naar de rug van Dik.
Die schrijft ook meteen het antwoord op.
Ik wil winnen! denkt Lotte.
Riko draait zich om.
Hij kijkt op haar blaadje.

Lotte houdt meteen haar hand erop.
Maar het is al te laat.
Riko heeft het al gezien.
'Riko', roept juf.
'Zelf denken!
Deze reken ik fout bij jou.'
Net goed, Riko de Piko, denkt Lotte.
Doe het maar mooi zelf.
Juf gaat nu in een hoog tempo.
Na twaalf sommen stopt ze.
'We kijken samen na', zegt ze.
'Geef je blaadje aan je buurman.'
De klas ruilt de blaadjes.
Miek en Lotte ruilen.
Lotte kijkt op het blaadje.
Juf schrijft de antwoorden op het bord.
Miek heeft zes sommen goed.
Lotte zet er een mooie krul bij.
Miek geeft Lotte haar blaadje.
'Twaalf goed', zegt ze verbaasd.
'Hoe doe je dat?
Wat zit er in jouw hoofd?'
Lotte haalt haar schouders op.
'Het gaat vanzelf.'
Ze lacht.
Alleen Dik en Lotte hebben alles goed.
'De kanjers van Sneltel', zegt juf.
'Wie krijgt deze mooie kaart?

Ik scheur hem niet in twee stukken.
Nog een ronde voor Dik en Lotte.
Ik geef jullie drie sommen.
Jullie schrijven het antwoord op.
Moeilijk of makkelijk?'
'Moeilijk', zeggen ze in koor.
'Pff', zegt Miek zacht.
'Dit was al moeilijk.'
Lotte gaat recht zitten.
Haar hart bonst een beetje.
Kan ze het winnen van Dik?
Hij is zo goed.
'Daar gaat-ie', zegt juf.
'Stilte in de klas graag.'
De klas is muisstil.
$7 \times 7 + 9 \times 7$.
Lotte schrijft 112 op.
Dik denkt nog, ziet ze.
Dan gaat juf alweer verder.
$88 - 45 + 32$.
Lotte denkt na.
Ze schrijft 75 op.
Is dat wel goed?
Ze heeft geen tijd meer.
Juf zegt de laatste som.
$7 \times 4 + 8 \times 3$.
Snel schrijft ze 52 op.
'Kom maar met jullie blaadjes', zegt juf.

Dik en Lotte staan samen voor de klas.
Even later kijkt juf de klas in.
Iedereen is stil.
'Dik had er twee goed en Lotte ...
drie!' zegt juf.
Juf geeft Lotte een hand. Dik ook.
'Knap gedaan, Lotte', zegt hij.
Juf geeft de kaart aan Lotte.
Ze legt hem op haar tafel.
Het is een leuke kaart.
Het lijkt wel of de apen lachen.

3 · Buurvrouw Berta

Lotte komt thuis.
Mama zet de borden net op tafel.
Papa en Joost zijn er niet.
Joost is op school. Hij is al dertien.
Papa is aan het werk. Hij is kok.
Hij heeft een eethuisje.
Lotte eet vier witte broodjes.
Het zijn broodjes met knakworst.
Op de knakworst spuit ze eerst mosterd.
Daarna doet ze er een laagje mayo over.
Lotte houdt niet van bruinbrood.
Het smaakt raar.
Mama eet bruinbrood.
'Hoe was het op school?' vraagt mama.
'Goed,' zegt Lotte, 'het was leuk.'
Dat zegt ze elke dag.
Ze wil niet over gym praten.
Mama kan er toch niks aan doen.
'Lotte', zegt mama.
'Papa vraagt of ik hem kom helpen.'
'Helpen?' vraagt Lotte.
'Waarom?'
Mama zucht.
'Het eethuisje loopt steeds beter.

Dat is fijn voor ons.
Er komen veel mensen eten.
Het eethuis zit elke dag propvol.
Papa werkt veel te hard.'
Lotte kijkt mama aan.
Mama helpt papa heel soms.
Ze vindt het leuk werk.
Lotte knikt.
'Ik eet wel bij buurvrouw Berta.'

Mama schudt haar hoofd.
'Dat kan niet.
Berta gaat twee maanden weg.'
'Weg?' vraagt Lotte verbaasd.
'Haar dochter heeft een baby', zegt mama.
'Die dochter woont in Ierland.
Zij wil ernaartoe.
Berta wil haar kleinkind zien.
Ze gaat haar dochter helpen.'
Lotte zucht hardop.
Buurvrouw Berta is erg aardig.
Lotte laat Max wel eens uit.
Max is de hond van Berta.
Hij is groot en sterk.
Maar hij luistert goed.
'Wat jammer', zegt Lotte.
'Neemt Berta Max mee?' vraagt ze.
Mama schudt haar hoofd.
'Ik denk het niet', zegt ze.
'Een baby en een hond samen?
Dat gaat niet altijd goed.'
'Als jij papa gaat helpen', zegt Lotte.
'Wat moet ik dan tussen de middag?'
'Daar zit ik juist mee', zegt mama.
'Wil je niet op school eten?'
Lotte schudt haar hoofd.
'Nee', zegt ze snel.
'Dat wil ik niet.'

4 · Miek

Het is een dag later.
Tussen de middag loopt Miek met Lotte mee.
Miek woont vlak bij Lotte.
'Mijn moeder gaat werken', vertelt Lotte.
'Het is zo druk in het eethuis.
Vooral tussen de middag.
Dan kan ik niet thuis eten.
Ik wil niet op school eten.'
Miek kijkt Lotte aan.
'Waarom niet?' vraagt ze verbaasd.
'Na het eten mag je naar het plein.
Leuk, lekker lang spelen!'
Lotte schudt haar hoofd.
'Riko eet ook op school.
Hij noemt mij nijlpaard.'
'Schelden is naar', zegt Miek.
'Vanbinnen doet het zeer.'
Ze zijn bij Lottes huis.
Miek steekt haar hand op.
'Doei!' roept ze.
Dan rent ze naar haar eigen huis.
Lotte kijkt haar na.
Miek rent vaak.
Lotte heeft een hekel aan rennen.

Mama zit aan tafel te wachten.
De broodjes knakworst zijn al klaar.
Lotte wast eerst haar handen.
Mama komt bij Lotte staan.
'Ik heb met Berta gepraat.
Ze neemt Max niet mee. Ze vroeg ...'
Mama stopt. Ze praat niet verder.
Ze wacht tot Lotte klaar is.
Lotte droogt snel haar handen af.
'Wat vroeg ze?' vraagt Lotte.
Ze wil het graag weten.
Ze gaat aan tafel zitten.
Dan vertelt mama verder.
'Wil jij voor Max zorgen, Lotte?'
'Ik?' Lotte is verbaasd.
'Ik ben nog maar acht jaar.
Maar ik wil het wel, mama. Max is zo lief!'
'Dat zei ik ook al', zegt mama.
'Jij bent nog maar acht.
Veel te jong, dat kan jij niet.
Ga straks even naar Berta toe.'
Lotte schrokt haar broodjes op.
Ze vergeet de mosterd en de mayo.
Daarna loopt ze naar Berta.
Lotte gaat achterom.
De tuindeur staat een beetje open.
Max ligt in de tuin.
Hij heeft een plekje in de schaduw.

Max houdt niet van de zon.
Hij blaft een paar keer.
'Koest Max', zegt Lotte streng.
Dat helpt meteen. Max komt naar Lotte toe.
Ze gaat op haar hurken zitten.
Max legt zijn kop op haar schouder.
Lotte legt haar armen om Max heen.
'Wat ben je toch een lieve hond.'
Lotte aait over zijn kop. Zo blijft ze even zitten.
Dan staat Lotte op.
Ze loopt naar binnen.

5 · Bijna negen

'Ha, die Lotte', zegt Berta.
'Ik had je al verwacht.'
Berta zit aan tafel te eten.
Lotte gaat ook aan tafel zitten.
Berta kijkt Lotte aan.
Ze legt haar mes en vork neer.
'Heeft mama het aan jou gevraagd?'
'Van Max?' vraagt Lotte.
'Of ik voor hem wil zorgen?'
Berta knikt.
'Wat vind jij daarvan?
Wil jij dat?'
'Ik wil het wel heel erg graag', zegt Lotte.
'Denkt u dat ik het kan?
Ik ben nog maar acht.'
Berta schudt haar hoofd.
'Je bent al bijna negen', zegt ze.
'Je bent een flinke meid.
Max luistert goed naar jou.'
Lotte knikt.
Dat is waar.
Ze kent Max al twee jaar.
Eerst was hij een jonge pup.
Hij leek op een knuffel.

Net zo zacht en schattig.
Max werd steeds groter.
Hij deed weleens stout.
Max beet een schoen kapot.
En hij plaste in de gang.
Berta was heel streng voor hem.
Max luistert nu goed.
Dat heeft hij geleerd van Berta.
Het is een fijne hond.
'Weet je wat?' zegt Berta.
'Ik heb een brief gemaakt.'
Berta geeft de brief aan Lotte.
Lottes handen trillen.
Wat spannend, een brief!
Wat zou erin staan?

'Wanneer wilt u het weten?' vraagt Lotte.
'Morgen?' vraagt Berta.
'Of vind je dat te snel?'
Lotte schudt haar hoofd.
'Morgen kan wel', zegt ze.
'Morgen na schooltijd.'
Berta gaat staan.
'Je moet zo weer naar school.'
Lotte kijkt naar de brief.
Op de voorkant staat: Voor Lotte.
Berta lacht naar haar.
'Maak hem maar na schooltijd open.
Nu lukt dat niet meer.

Dan kom je te laat op school.
Een boze juf is niet fijn.'
Lotte moet lachen.
'Juf is nooit boos op mij', zegt ze.
'Ik doe altijd goed mijn best.
Ik kan alles goed.
Alleen gym kan ik niet.'

6 · Nog een brief

Lotte is weer thuis.
Ze legt de brief op tafel.
Nog een kwartier.
Dan gaat de schoolbel.
Snel geeft ze mama een kus.
Ze wijst naar de brief.
'Ik lees hem als ik terug ben.
Ik moet nu naar school.'
Mama knikt.
'Wat staat erin?' vraagt ze.
Lotte geeft geen antwoord.
Ze roept alleen:
'Doeg mama, tot straks!'
En weg is ze.

De bel gaat.
Lotte is net op het plein.
Ze kan meteen naar binnen.
Juf staat voor de klas.
Ze heeft brieven in haar hand.
Het is een hele stapel.
Ze legt de stapel op het bureau.
Juf steekt haar hand omhoog.
Het duurt maar een paar tellen.

Dan is de klas stil.
'Ik wil iets zeggen over deze brieven.
Elk kind krijgt een brief mee.
Het is een brief van de schooldokter.
Daar moeten jullie naartoe.
Samen met je vader of je moeder.
De schooldokter kijkt of je gezond bent.
Hij kijkt hoe lang je bent.
En hoe zwaar je bent.
Hij luistert naar je longen.
Hij wil weten of je goed hoort.
En of je ogen goed zijn.'
Bah, denkt Lotte.
Naar de dokter.
Dan moet je op de weegschaal staan.
Daar is niks aan.
In groep twee was dat ook zo.
Ze weet het nog goed.
Mama ging mee.
Ze zeurde daarna heel erg.
'Minder snoepen, Lotte.
Dat zegt de dokter.
Je moet aan sport doen, Lotte.
Dat zegt de dokter.'
Mama zeurde een paar weken.
Toen hield ze ermee op.
Het hielp toch niks.
Nu moet ze weer naar de dokter!

Straks gaat mama weer zeuren.
Bah!
Juf legt de brief op Lottes tafel.
Er duwt iemand tegen haar rug.
Lotte draait zich om.
Het is Riko.
Hij zit vlak achter haar.

'Nou nijlpaard met je speknek', fluistert hij.
'Jij gaat ook op de weegschaal.
Dat moet bij die dokter.
De weegschaal gaat vast kapot.
Een nijlpaard houdt hij niet.
Boing! Krak!'
Riko maakt een raar geluid.
Hij doet de weegschaal na.
Riko doet het heel zacht.
Juf Ank deelt de brieven uit.
Ze heeft niks door.
Lotte draait zich om.
Haar hoofd is rood.
Er willen tranen naar buiten.
Ze knippert met haar ogen.
Niet huilen, denkt ze boos.
Riko vindt het leuk als ik huil.
Dat wil ik niet!
Ze zegt niks terug tegen Riko.
Kan een weegschaal stukgaan?
Lotte staat nooit op een weegschaal.
Thuis wil ze er niet op.
Het hoeft nooit van mama.
Zou het bij de dokter wel moeten?

7 · Zeuren

Langzaam loopt Lotte naar huis.
Ze heeft de brief in haar hand.
Ik gooi hem weg, denkt ze.
Ik begraaf hem.
Ik verscheur hem. Ik ...
Hou maar op.
Het kan niet, denkt ze.
Mama komt het toch te weten.
Miek rent haar voorbij.
Zij heeft ook een brief.
'Ha die Lotte', roept ze.
Ze zwaait met haar brief.
Lotte kijkt haar na.
'Rotbrief', zegt ze hardop.
Thuis gooit ze de brief op tafel.
Mama leest de krant.
Ze kijkt op.
'Wat is er?' vraagt ze.
'Niks', zegt Lotte kwaad.
'Alleen deze brief.
Dat is alles.
Hij komt van de schooldokter.
Daar moet ik heen.
Ik wil er niet heen.'

Mama legt de krant weg.
Ze leest wat er in de brief staat.
Dan legt mama de brief op tafel.
Lotte kijkt mama aan.
'Weet je het nog?' vraagt ze boos.
'Het was in groep twee.
Je zeurde zo, mama.
Over snoepen en over sport.
Het was niet leuk.'
Mama knikt.
'Ik weet het nog.

Maar ik vond het ook niet leuk.'
'Jij ook niet?' vraagt Lotte.
Ze is verbaasd.
Mama knikt.
'Je was zo knorrig.
En zo boos.
Je wilde snoep.
Je wilde nooit fruit.
Je zeurde maar door.
Ik kon er niet goed tegen.
Papa gaf jou gelijk.
Hij is ook te dik.
Toen hield ik maar op.'
Mama kijkt naar Lotte.
Het gezicht van mama staat boos.
Ze haalt haar schouders op.
'Als de dokter iets vraagt, dan ...'
Ze stopt even met praten.
'Nou?' vraagt Lotte.
'Wat zeg je dan?'
Mama schudt haar hoofd.
'Dat zeg ik niet', zegt mama.
'Ik praat wel met de dokter.'
Het is stil in de kamer.
Lotte kijkt naar mama.
Mama kijkt nog steeds boos.
Zie je wel, denkt Lotte.
Het komt door die brief.

Nu zijn we boos op elkaar.
Bah! Dit wil ik niet!
Ik geef de brief aan Max.
Dan bijt hij de brief wel stuk!
Ineens denkt Lotte aan iets anders.
'Waar is de brief van buurvrouw?'
Mama tilt de krant op.
'Hier ligt hij', zegt ze.
'Lees hem maar gauw.'
Lotte gaat op de bank zitten.
Snel scheurt ze de brief open.

8 · Marmot

Lieve Lotte,
Wat doe ik elke dag met Max?
Ik laat hem uit.
Twee keer lang.
En twee keer kort.
Dat is dus vier keer!
Om 7 uur in de ochtend.
Tussen de middag om 12 uur.
Om 5 uur, vlak voor het eten.
Om 11 uur, voor ik ga slapen.
Ik loop twee keer een uur met hem.
En twee keer een kwartier.
Max wil graag rennen en lopen.
Dat heeft hij echt nodig.
Ik borstel hem ook.
Dat doe ik een keer per week.
Anders heb je overal haar!
Twee keer per dag krijgt hij eten.
Dat is vlak voor ik hem uitlaat.
Hij heeft altijd schoon water.
Hij drinkt wanneer hij wil.
Dat was het, Lotte.
Denk je dat je het kan?
Groetjes, buurvrouw Berta.

'Ja', zegt Lotte hardop.
'Ja, ik wil het en ik kan het!'
'Wat staat erin?' vraagt mama.
'Lees maar', zegt Lotte.
Even later kijkt mama haar aan.
'Ze laat hem vaak uit', zegt ze.
'Dat kost veel tijd.
Ik vind het niet goed, Lotte.
Je bent veel te jong.
Max ziet er ook eng uit.
Die grote, scherpe tanden.
Soms blaft hij zo hard.'
Mama is al groot, denkt Lotte.
Toch vindt ze Max eng.
Raar is dat.
'Je moet voor schooltijd lopen', zegt mama.
'Een uur, dat lukt nooit.'
Lotte denkt even na.
'Ik moet er om tien voor zeven uit.'
'En zelf de wekker zetten', zegt mama.
'Vroeg eruit, dat is niks voor jou.'
Lotte denkt na.
Haar bed is altijd zo lekker warm.
Vroeg eruit is niet fijn.
Mama kijkt Lotte ernstig aan.
'Twee maanden is te lang.
Een week, dat is te doen.
Twee maanden, nee.'

Mama schudt haar hoofd.
Lotte wordt boos.
'Raar', zegt ze.
'Ik moet aan sport doen.
Dat zeg je zo vaak.
Lopen met een hond is ook gezond.
Je wordt er sterk van.'
Ze stampt kwaad met haar voet.
Mama kijkt naar Lotte.
'Je hebt gelijk', zegt ze.
'Maar ik dacht aan jou.
Hoe moeilijk je uit bed komt.
Je bent net een marmot.'
Lotte moet lachen.
Al wil ze dat niet.
Dan kijkt ze weer ernstig.
'Voor Max doe ik het', zegt ze.
'Hij is zo blij als hij mij ziet.'
Mama loopt naar Lotte.
Ze pakt Lottes hand.
'Ik ben ook blij als ik jou zie.
Alleen blaf ik niet.'
Lotte geeft mama een dikke knuffel.
'Ik ga het doen', zegt Lotte.
'Ik wil het gewoon.'
Mama is stil. Ze kijkt Lotte aan.
Dan begint ze te lachen.
'Je bent net papa', zegt ze.

'Als hij iets in zijn hoofd heeft,
houden tien paarden hem niet tegen.'
Maar ...'
Ze wacht even.
'Ik ga je niet roepen.
En ik wil ook geen gezeur.
Afspraak?'
'Afspraak', zegt Lotte.

9 · Twee stenen

Lotte laat Max uit.
Dat doet ze met buurvrouw Berta.
Ze lopen op de stoep.
Max rent voor hen uit.
Hij kijkt telkens om.
Buurvrouw loopt flink door.
Ze doen de grote ronde.
Die ronde duurt een uur.
Lotte wordt moe.
Ze voelt een steek in haar zij.
'Niet zo snel', hijgt ze.
Berta kijkt haar aan.
'Snel?' vraagt ze.
'Dit is niet snel.'
Toch loopt ze niet meer zo vlug.
De stoep wordt een zandpad.
Het pad loopt langs een speeltuin.
Lotte schrikt.
Boven op het klimrek zit Riko.
Riko zegt niks.
Hij kijkt alleen maar.
Lotte kijkt weer gauw voor zich.
Ze hoeft hem niet te zien.
Dan hoort ze het.

'Ha nijlpaard', roept hij.
'Loop je met je oma?'
'Zegt hij nijlpaard?' vraagt Berta.
Haar stem klinkt kwaad.
Lotte knikt.
Er staan tranen in haar ogen.
'Riko vindt mij een dikzak.
Hij zegt nooit Lotte.
Hij noemt me ook vetzak of speknek.'
Berta zegt een hele tijd niks.
Ze lopen weer flink door.
Ineens staat Berta stil.
Ze wijst naar een bult stenen.
De bult ligt naast het zandpad.
Het zijn oude, ronde stenen.
Er groeit wat gras tussen.
'Wil je twee stenen pakken?'
Lotte knikt.
Ze is verbaasd.
Wat wil Berta ermee doen?
Toch pakt ze twee stenen.
Ze zijn zwaar.
Berta houdt er een vast.
Ze weegt de steen in haar hand.
'Drie kilo', zegt ze.
'Wil jij ze voor me dragen?'
'Ik?' schrikt Lotte.
Berta lacht een beetje.

'Ik gebruik ze in de tuin.'
'Waarom moet ik ze dragen?' vraagt Lotte boos.
'Omdat ik het aan je vraag', zegt Berta.
'Kun je de stenen naar huis dragen?'
Lotte zucht. De stenen zijn zwaar.
Ze sjokt achter Berta aan.
De stenen worden steeds zwaarder.
Het is nog een heel eind naar huis!
Lotte blijft staan en hijgt.
Ze is boos. Op de stenen en op Berta.
Ze kijkt naar de rug van Berta.
Berta draait zich om.

Ze kijkt Lotte vragend aan.
Maar Lotte gooit de stenen weg.
Ze rollen in de bosjes.
'Lukte het niet meer?' vraagt Berta.
'Nee', zegt Lotte kwaad.
'Mijn armen doen zeer.
Samen wegen ze wel zes kilo!'
Berta kijkt Lotte aan.
Ze legt haar hand op Lottes haar.
'Jij sjouwt wel drie stenen mee.
Ze liggen niet in de bosjes.
Ze zitten aan je lijf.
Daarom ben je zo gauw moe.
Je gooit die stenen in de bosjes.
Dat kun je met tien kilo niet doen.'
Kalm loopt ze naar de bosjes.
Daar zoekt ze de stenen.
Lotte kijkt naar de rug van Berta.
'Daar kan ik niks aan doen!
U mag dat niet zeggen', schreeuwt Lotte.
Berta heeft de stenen in haar handen.
Ze kijkt Lotte recht aan.
'Weet je, Lotte', zegt ze.
'Het is jouw lijf.
Jij kunt er iets aan doen.
Kom op, we gaan naar huis.
Ik draag de stenen.
Ze zullen heel mooi staan in de tuin.'

10 · De weegschaal

Die avond kan Lotte niet slapen.
Ze denkt steeds aan de stenen.
Ze waren zo zwaar!
Ik sjouw drie stenen mee, denkt Lotte.
Twee stenen zijn al zwaar!
Drie stenen zijn nog zwaarder.
Was het gemeen van Berta?
Of heeft ze gelijk?
Het duurt lang voor Lotte in slaap valt.
De volgende morgen gaat mama mee naar school.
Ze zijn als eerste aan de beurt.
De dokter is een mevrouw. Ze is heel aardig.
Ze praten eerst een tijdje.
Lotte moet door een bril kijken.
Haar ogen zijn goed.
Ze gaat bij de meetlat staan.
De dokter zegt: '1 meter 35.'
Dan komt de weegschaal.
De wijzer gaat heen en weer.
Hij knalt niet uit elkaar!
De dokter zegt: '45 kilo.'
Ze kijkt Lotte aan.
'Mag ik nog even met mama praten?
Dan wacht jij op de gang.'

'Nee', zegt Lotte.
'Ik weet het heus wel. U vindt mij te dik.
Daar kan mama niks aan doen.
Ik ga niet naar de gang. Ik wil erbij zijn.'
De dokter kijkt naar Lotte.
'Goed', zegt ze dan.
'Blijf maar hier.
Je bent te zwaar, Lotte.
Doe je ook aan sport?'

'Nee,' zegt Lotte, 'niks aan.'
De dokter schrijft iets op.
'Kun je zeggen wat je eet?'
'Wanneer?' vraagt Lotte.
'De hele dag', zegt de dokter.
Lotte knikt.
'Ik ontbijt met brood', zegt ze.
'Vier broodjes met pasta.
In de pauze eet ik een zakje koek.
En een beker yoki.
Tussen de middag ...'
Lotte stopt en kijkt naar mama.
Mama kijkt haar niet aan.
'Eet ik vier broodjes knakworst.'
'Hoeveel knakworst?' vraagt de dokter.
'Een heel blikje', zegt Lotte.
'En twee glazen yoki.
Uit school thee met koek.'
'Hoeveel koekjes?' vraagt de dokter.
'Zo veel als ik wil', zegt Lotte.
'Warm eten is altijd anders.
Dan eet ik een bord.
Als we friet eten, twee borden.'
'Eet je fruit en groente?'
De dokter kijkt Lotte ernstig aan.
Lotte schudt haar hoofd.
'Nee, dat smaakt raar.'
De dokter schrijft weer iets op.

Dan kijkt ze Lotte aan.
'Zou je anders willen eten?'
Lotte schudt haar hoofd.
'Dan heb ik honger.'
De dokter kijkt mama aan.
'Wat vindt u ervan?'
Mama haalt haar schouders op.
'Ze zeurt altijd over eten.
Ik kan niet tegen haar op.
Dan geef ik Lotte haar zin.'
Lotte kijkt de dokter aan.
'Riko noemt mij nijlpaard.
Anna zegt dat ik uit mijn broek knap.
Dat is niet leuk.'
'Dat heb je nooit verteld', zegt mama.
'Tuurlijk niet', zegt Lotte.
'Dan ga jij weer zeuren.'
De dokter kijkt op de klok.
'Ik geef je een boekje mee', zegt ze.
'Wil je het eens lezen?
Je hebt maar een lijf.
Daar doe je je hele leven mee.
Je mag er zuinig op zijn.
Er goed voor zorgen.'
De dokter geeft Lotte een hand.
'Tot ziens', zegt ze.
'Je bent een slimme meid, Lotte.
Denk maar eens na over het boekje.'

11 · Yoki

Mama en Lotte lopen naar de klas.
'Thuis praten we verder', zegt mama.
Lotte gaat het lokaal in.
Riko prikt in haar rug.
'Is de weegschaal nog heel?'
Lotte zegt niks.
Ze doet haar schrift open.
'Krak, boing', fluistert Riko.
Hij prikt nog eens.
Lotte bladert in het boekje.
Het boekje ziet er leuk uit.
Plaatjes van meisjes die lachen en spelen.
Jongens die rennen en zwemmen.
Lotte begint te lezen:
'Eet genoeg fruit en groente! Beweeg!
Elke dag in ieder geval een half uur.
Fietsen, buiten spelen, sport.
Lopen of rennen met de hond.
Alles is goed.'
Ha, denkt Lotte.
Voor Max zorgen is dus een goed idee.
Juf loopt langs.
'Lees dat thuis maar, Lotte', zegt ze streng.
'Nu is het tijd voor taal.'

Tussen de middag is er geen knakworst.
Mama zet drie broodjes met jam neer.
'Morgen ga ik werken', zegt mama.
'Jij eet dan bij Miek.'
Lotte hapt van haar brood.
'Bij Miek?' vraagt ze.
'Die moeder is zo streng.'
'Dat maakt niet uit', zegt mama.
'En ik betaal haar ervoor.
Jij eet daar voortaan tussen de middag.'
'Elke dag?' vraagt Lotte.
Mama knikt.
'Op zaterdag en zondag niet.'
Lotte is boos. Ze eet haar brood op.
Dan schuift ze haar bord naar voren.
'Nog twee broodjes', zegt ze.
Mama schudt haar hoofd.
'Nee', zegt ze streng.
'Deze keer hou ik het vol.
Hoe jij ook zeurt. Ik zet het door.
Geen knakworst en koek meer.'
Lotte is woedend.
'Zie je wel', gilt ze.
'Dat komt door die dokter.
Ik zei het toch?'
Mama kijkt Lotte aan.
'Wil je zo dik blijven?'
Lotte haalt haar schouders op.

Dan pakt ze haar beker.
Er zit appelsap in.
'Waar is de yoki?' schreeuwt ze.
Mama wijst naar de gootsteen.
'Daar', zegt ze.
'Voortaan krijg jij sap.'
Ruw duwt Lotte de beker opzij.
Hij valt om. Het sap drupt op de grond.

Mama is boos.
Ze pakt een doek.
Daarmee dept ze het sap op.
Ze pakt de beker van Lotte.
Die houdt ze onder de kraan.
'Water', zegt ze.
'Drink dat dan maar.'
Lotte is kwaad.
Maar ze heeft ook dorst.
Ze drinkt de beker leeg.
'Ik ga naar Berta', zegt ze kwaad.
'Naar Max.
Nog een dag en dan is ze weg.
Jij doet toch stom tegen mij.
Er is hier niks aan.'
Berta is blij als ze Lotte ziet.
Ze lopen een kort rondje met Max.
Lotte moet straks weer naar school.
'Hoe was het bij de dokter?' vraagt Berta.
'U had gelijk', zegt Lotte.
'De dokter zegt het en mama ook.'
'En jij?' zegt buurvrouw.
'Wat vind jij?'
'Ik wil niet dik zijn', zucht Lotte.
'Maar ik hou zo veel van eten.'
'Mooi', lacht buurvrouw.
'Je denkt erover na.
Dat is een goed begin.'

12 · Snotkop

Om tien voor zeven gaat de wekker.
Lotte is meteen wakker.
Ze springt uit bed.
Vlug kleedt ze zich aan.
Max wacht op haar!
Hij woont nu bij Lotte.
Ze loopt de trap af.
Op de wc doet ze een plas.
Max is blij als hij haar ziet.
Hij kwispelt met zijn staart.
Hij moet ook een plas.
Lotte drinkt een glas sap.
Er is niks anders in de koelkast.
Ze geeft Max een schaaltje brokken.
Hij schrokt ze op.
Lotte smeert snel een bruin broodje.
Ze ziet nergens witbrood.
Dan pakt ze de riem.
Max loopt al voor haar uit.
Bij de deur blijft hij staan.
Hij kijkt om naar Lotte.
'Brave hond', zegt ze zacht.
'Kom, we gaan.'
Het is nog vroeg.

De straat is stil.
Lotte loopt goed door.
Ze doet een ronde van een uur.
Dat kan net.
Ze moeten de straat over.

'Hier Max', zegt ze.
Hij komt meteen.
Ze klopt op zijn hals.
'Wat luister je toch goed.'
Ze maakt de riem vast.
Ze lacht hardop.
Het is fijn buiten met Max.
Bij een veld mag hij los.
Hij rent voor Lotte uit.
Dan komt hij weer terug.
Dat doet hij de hele tijd.
Zijn tong hangt uit zijn bek.
Om acht uur is Lotte weer thuis.
Max drinkt uit zijn bak.
Lotte neemt nog een glas water.
Mama komt de trap af.
Ze is net uit bed.
Ze wrijft in haar ogen.
'Knap hoor', zegt ze.
'Je bent zelf uit bed gegaan.'
Ze strijkt Lotte over het haar.
Lotte wast zich snel.
Dan poetst ze haar tanden.
Het is tijd voor school.
In de klas voelt Lotte het pas.
Haar benen zijn erg moe.
Maar dat geeft niet.
In de klas rust ze mooi uit.

Het is pauze.
Lotte pakt haar tas.
Ze doet de tas open.
Dan ziet ze een appel.
Nee! Geen koekjes.
'Hé nijlpaard', fluistert Riko.
'Waar is je koek, speknek?
Je moet flink koek eten.
Dat is goed voor je speknek.'
Miek loopt net langs.
Ze hoort wat Riko zegt.
'Snotkop, hou je mond', zegt Miek.
Riko wordt boos.
Hij trekt aan de trui van Miek.
'Bemoei je er niet mee', zegt hij.
'Ik ben geen snotkop.'
'Jawel', zegt Miek.
'Je hebt altijd een snotneus.
Je veegt het af aan je mouw.
Een snotkop met een groene mouw.
Bah! Neem een zakdoek mee.'
Juf kijkt naar hen.
'Is er wat, Riko?' vraagt ze.
Riko haalt zijn neus op.
'Nee hoor', zegt hij.
'Miek en ik maken een praatje.'
Lotte kijkt naar haar appel.
Ze kijkt Riko aan.

Dan neemt ze een grote hap.
'Ik eet deze appel op, snotkop.'
Ze lacht als ze het zegt.
Snotkop is een leuk woord.
Weg met het vet, denkt ze.
Ik wil geen nijlpaard zijn.
'Ik krijg je nog wel', fluistert Riko.
'Wacht jij maar af.'

13 · Het lied van juf

Lotte eet bij Miek.
Ze eten warm.
Er is sla en witlof.
Dat lust ik niet, denkt Lotte.
Ze durft niks te zeggen.
De moeder van Miek is streng.
Lotte eet de sla en de witlof op.
Het valt mee.
De witlof is een beetje bitter.
Na het eten gaat Lotte naar huis.
Miek gaat met haar mee.
Ze heeft een sleutel.
Lotte doet de deur open.
Max springt op.
Samen lopen ze naar buiten.
Miek heeft een stok bij zich.
Bij het veld gooit ze hem weg.
Max haalt hem steeds op.
Hij rent heen en weer.
Max legt de stok bij Lotte neer.
Niet bij Miek.
'Hij kent jou', zegt Miek.
'Daarom doet hij dat.
Wat is hij toch lief.'

Lotte lacht.
Ze is trots op Max.
'We moeten terug', zegt ze.
'Het is tijd.'
Ze doet Max aan de riem.

Snel lopen ze naar huis.
Max gaat weer in de keuken.
Dan lopen ze meteen door.
Miek wil naar school rennen.
Lotte wil dat niet.
'Ren jij maar', zegt ze.
'Ik kom wel.'
Miek rent al weg.
Ze wil nog voetballen.
Lotte sjokt achter haar aan.
Haar benen zijn erg moe.
Ze is net op tijd.
Riko is er niet.
'Hij is naar de dokter', zegt juf.
'Elk kind komt aan de beurt.
Zo gaat het de hele week door.'
Ze zucht.
Het is wel een gedoe.
Er mist telkens een kind.
Het ene kind mist taal.
Een ander kind schrijven.
Een ander verkeer.
Miek steekt haar vinger op.
'Is elk kind goedgekeurd?' vraagt ze.
Juf moet erom lachen.
Ze begint zomaar een lied te zingen.
'We hebben allemaal wat.
We zijn allemaal raar.'

Lotte kijkt naar juf.
Is dat zo?
Heeft elk kind wel iets?
Het lied is uit.
Dik steekt een vinger op.
'Ik kon het niet goed zien.
Misschien moet ik wel een bril.'
Miek steekt een vinger op.
'Ik word lang, zegt de dokter.
En ik ben te dun.'
Anna doet haar vinger omhoog.
'Ik ben te klein voor mijn leeftijd.
Ik moet nog eens terugkomen.'
'Ik ook', roept Miek.
'Ik ook', zegt Dik.
Els steekt ook haar vinger omhoog.
'Er is iets met mijn voeten.
Ze staan niet goed recht.'
Juf lacht naar de klas.
'God maakte elk kind.
Hij is blij met je.
Het maakt niet uit wat je hebt.'
Miek kijkt naar Lotte.
Ze geeft Lotte een knipoog.
Lotte wordt ineens blij vanbinnen.

14 · Klimrek

Het is nog geen zeven uur.
Lotte heeft al kleren aan.
Ineens staat papa voor haar in de gang.
Hij heeft alleen een onderbroek aan.
Zijn ogen zijn nog half dicht.
Zijn haar staat alle kanten op.
'Ik ga met je mee', geeuwt hij.
'Waarom?' vraagt Lotte.
Papa wrijft in zijn ogen.
'Ik vind het zo knap van je.
Je doet het al weken zonder zeuren.'
'Dat hoeft niet', zegt Lotte snel.
'Ik vind het leuk om te doen.
Daarom houd ik het zo goed vol.
Ga maar weer terug naar bed.
Jij laat Max elke avond uit.
Jij zeurt toch ook niet?'
Papa trekt Lotte tegen zich aan.
'Jij bent mijn grote kanjer', zegt hij.
Lotte prikt in zijn dikke buik.
'En jij bent mijn dikke kanjer.'
Papa lacht hard.
'Dag lief schatje patatje', lacht hij.
Dan draait hij zich om.

Hij sjokt de trap weer op.
Buiten kijkt Lotte naar Max.
Hij loopt netjes naast haar.
Lotte voelt aan haar broek.
Hij zit veel te los.
Er moet nu een riem omheen.
Dat komt van alle uren lopen.
Bij het veld laat Lotte Max los.
Lotte rent een eindje met hem mee.
Het is fijn om met hem te rennen!
Bij het veld staat een rond klimrek.
Lotte klimt er bovenop.
Max ziet nog een hond.
Samen rennen ze over het veld.
Ze happen naar elkaar.
De honden rollen over elkaar.
Het is maar een spel.
De honden vinden het leuk.
Dan hoort ze een stem.
'Hé nijlpaard, wat doe jij hier?
Van mijn klimrek af.'
Lotte draait zich om.
Het is Riko.
Hij staat achter haar op de grond.
'Ik ga er niet af', zegt ze kwaad.
'Dat klimrek is niet van jou!'
Snel klimt Riko naar boven.
Daar geeft hij Lotte een harde duw.

Lotte houdt zich niet goed vast.
Ze valt tussen het rek door.
Bam! Haar lijf smakt op de grond.
Even draait alles om Lotte heen.
Ze blijft stil liggen met haar ogen dicht.
Dan doet ze haar ogen open.
Ze kijkt in het gezicht van Riko.
'Moet je hier maar niet komen.'

Zijn stem klinkt vals.
'Dit is mijn plek.'
Lotte voelt ineens de snuit van Max.
Hij likt haar wang.
Met zijn snuit duwt hij tegen Lotte.
Hij wil dat ze opstaat.
Lotte staat op.
Maar alles doet zeer.
'Ga weg, nijlpaard', zegt Riko.
'Neem die rothond mee.'
Max kijkt omhoog naar Riko.
Hij gromt zacht.
Zijn lippen zijn omhoog.
Max laat zijn tanden zien.
Lotte kijkt naar Riko.
Hij heeft een wit gezicht.
Riko is bang voor Max!
Ineens krijgt Lotte een idee.
'Max kan je nu niet pakken', zegt ze.
'Maar ik neem hem mee naar school.
Hij is dol op jongens met snot.
Max heeft scherpe tanden.
Hij bijt jouw snotneus er zo af.'
'Die hond mag niet in school', piept Riko.
Lotte steekt haar tong uit naar Riko.
'Max mag niet in school.
Hij mag wel voor de school komen.'
Ze streelt de kop van Max.

Samen lopen ze weg.
Ze kijkt niet meer om.
'Stop!' gilt Riko.
'Ik scheld je niet meer uit.'
Lotte draait zich om.
'Dat spreken we af!' roept ze.
'Jij zegt Lotte tegen mij!'
Dan loopt ze door.

15 · Een cadeau

Lotte staat bij de voordeur.
Het is nog vroeg.
Ze wacht op Berta.
Er stopt een taxi voor hun huis.
Berta stapt eruit!
Max rent door de gang naar buiten.
Hij is door het dolle heen.
Berta laat haar tassen staan.
Ze gaat op haar hurken zitten.
Ze knuffelt Max.
Lotte kijkt naar Max en Berta.
Het is voorbij met Max, denkt ze.
Berta draait zich om.
Lotte krijgt ook een knuffel.
'Ben je niet blij?' vraagt Berta.
Lotte schudt haar hoofd.
'Het was zo fijn met Max.
Nu is het voorbij.'
Berta lacht naar Lotte.
'Je hebt goed voor hem gezorgd.
Ik heb een mooi cadeau voor jou.
Eerst belde ik je ouders.
Zij vonden het goed.
Laat me eens naar je kijken.

Ik zie bijna geen buik meer.
Waar is die?'
'Weg', lacht Lotte.
'Ik liep elke dag met Max.
En ik eet bij de moeder van Miek.
Die is streng, maar ook aardig.'
'Geen knakworst meer?' lacht Berta.

Lotte schudt haar hoofd.
Mama komt ook naar buiten.
Ze is nog maar net uit bed.
Haar haren zitten nog in de war.
Mama geeft Berta een kus.
'Waar is ze?' vraagt Berta.
Ze kijkt om zich heen.
'In de schuur', lacht mama.
Ze doet de deur open.
Lotte snapt er niks van.
'Wie is er in de schuur?' vraagt ze.
Dan begint Max te blaffen.
Uit de schuur klinkt ook geblaf.
Er zit een hond in de schuur!
Lotte rent naar buiten.
Ze rukt de schuurdeur open.
In de schuur staat een hond.
De hond rent naar Lotte.
Daar blijft ze staan.
Haar kop schuin omhoog.
Berta staat naast Lotte.
'Zij is voor jou', zegt Berta.
Lotte kan niks zeggen.
Ze gelooft het niet.
'Het is echt waar', zegt mama.
'Papa haalde haar op.'
'Het is een spaniël', zegt Berta.
'Ze luistert goed.

Ze was van mijn vriendin.
Die vond haar veel te druk.
Ze wil rennen en spelen.
Ze heet Koosje.
Wat denk je ervan?'
'O ja', roept Lotte dan.
'Ik wil Koosje wel.
Ik zorg goed voor haar.
Net zoals voor Max.
Ze kunnen samen spelen.'
Lotte aait Koosje over haar kop.
Wat is ze mooi.
Wat ziet ze er lief uit.
Max loopt naar Koosje toe.
Hij snuffelt aan haar neus.
Hij ruikt aan haar staart.
Koosje loopt achter Max aan.
Ze draaien rondjes in de tuin.
Het is een leuk gezicht.
'Max en Koosje zijn al vrienden.'
Berta lacht als ze dat zegt.
Lotte legt haar arm om Berta heen.
'Ik heb een eigen hond', zegt ze.
'Van mij alleen.'
'Kom Koosje', roept ze.
Koosje komt meteen.
'Ze luistert goed', zegt mama.
Lotte slaat ook een arm om mama.

Zo staan ze even te kijken.
'Ik ben zo blij', zegt Lotte dan.
Ze geeft mama en Berta een kus.
Mama lacht.
'Het was niet mijn idee.
Het was het idee van Berta.
Maar het was een goed idee!'

MISTAKES WE KNEW WE WERE MAKING

NOTES

CORRECTIONS

CLARIFICATIONS

APOLOGIES

ADDENDA

MISTAKES WE KNEW WE WERE MAKING
Begun November 1998
Let go October 2000
First published 2001 by Vintage Books, a division of Random House, Inc., New York

First published in Great Britain 2001 by Picador
an imprint of Macmillan Publishers Ltd
25 Eccleston Place, London SW1W 9NF
Basingstoke and Oxford
Associated companies throughout the world
www.macmillan.com

Funny story about the chart used at the beginning of the book's other side: The chart, which listed the author as a 3 on
a scale of gay to straight, was for whatever reason taken much, much more seriously than had been intended. And the
interpretations were much too creative for comfort. There were a number of letters from AIDS educators who were very
concerned about the author's later statement as to having had a few unprotected encounters. One AIDS educator posited
that because a 3 was cited, it followed that 30 percent of the author's sexual encounters were with men, and because the
unsafe experiences were mentioned, that I was having many unsafe encounters with many men. Romantic, but untrue.
Look now, outside: the kids with the bikes are riding down the hill, screaming.

Now:

I have never been so tired.

You have:

No idea how tired I am.

I truly hope:

You are not as tired as I am.

OKAY NOW.

This edition of *A.H.W.O.S.G.* contains countless changes, sentence by sentence, many additions to the body of the text, and it also contains this, an appendix, featuring corrections, notations, updates, tangential remarks and clarifications. This appendix, you might be interested to know, was supposed to, and almost did, accompany the original hardcover edition of the book. A version of it was nearly complete, when its author made the mistake of telling a writer friend about it, with, let's admit, a certain smugness. I was, I figured, the first to think of adding a corrective appendix to a nonfiction work, one meant to illuminate the many factual and temporal fudgings necessary to keep this, or really any, work of nonfiction, from dragging around in arcana and endless explanations of who was exactly where, and when, etc. So: the corrective appendix was being prepared, and was to follow the original text, a few pages after the final "finally." But upon telling this writer-friend about the idea, she said, while looking much too ravishing over an open candle and with wet hair, "Oh, right, like Mary McCarthy." There was, in the distance, the sound of thunder, and of lightning striking, presumably, a kitten. "Um, what do you mean, pray tell, *Just like Mary McCarthy*?" I thought, while, fear-stricken, managing only "Huh?" She noted that McCarthy had done almost the same thing in *Memories of a Catholic Girlhood*, a book about which I was of course unware, because I am a moron. She explained that after each chapter

recounting various episodes from McCarthy's youth, there was a slightly shorter chapter, set in italics, wherein the author dismantled the
narrative, in favor of the unshaped truth.

Each corrective chapter, the writer-friend pointed out, began with
something like: *Well, it didn't happen exactly that way...* And this was
exactly my goal in adding the appendix in the first place: it afforded
the opportunity to be completely factual about things that in the narrative had to be compressed or altered slightly so the book could continue apace. But after this illuminating dinner, I sought and found a
copy of McCarthy's book (paperback edition with horrific cover), and
after reading McCarthy's perfect execution of the idea, I abandoned my
own appendix, not wanting to invest too much in a notion already
used. And besides, I felt, the stupid goddamn book was obviously long
enough. Thus, about 40 pages of prime appendix were scrapped.

But now, about eight brutal and then exhilarating and then more-
brutal-than-before months after the book was originally published,
I've gone ahead and finished the appendix, for better or worse, much
because it was heartily encouraged by this paperback version's diligent
and inspiring editor, Ms. Jenny Minton. But first please note: If you
did not like the Acknowledgments section, you will not like this. If
you liked the Acknowledgments section, then chances are you will like
this, unless your tastes have changed, in which case I am not sure what
you will think. In either case, this appendix contains the following:

a) CORRECTIONS: This element has already been spoken about. In
many places, where I've had to or chose to round the truth up or down,
I have here set the record perfectly straight. Most of these corrections,
however, are relevant only to the book's first half or so, since the second half of the book was harder to look at at this point, thus has been
left largely intact.

b) CLARIFICATIONS: In the next 40 pages or so, I'm pretty much
going to go ahead and explain much of the book, albeit often in very
small type.

c) UPDATES: Many passages or words or names in the main text
have given rise to updates about the whereabouts and howabouts of
certain characters or places. People always ask, for instance, about how

Shalini is doing, or how Toph is faring, etc. Herein are some, but not all, of the applicable answers. Briefly, about those characters not mentioned elsewhere in the appendix: Bill: fine; Beth: fine; Zev/Paul/ Moodie/Marny/Lance: fine; Kirsten: fine; John: still looking for the answer, or the silver bullet.

POINTS TO KEEP IN MIND:

a) *This appendix need not be read to understand or enjoy the book proper.* It is only for: 1) the author; 2) those with extra time; 3) those with interest disproportionate to what is warranted.

b) *These addenda were written at different times.* Though most of this section was written, or at least revised, at the same time—September 2000—a few parts of the appendix were written much earlier, and have been left as they were, and their period of origination is indicated.

c) *The number of changes to the text was, a few pages ago, hugely exaggerated.* The plan was to impose many many more changes and corrections, but when it came down to it, I just couldn't, at this point, spend much time in the main text. It was uncomfortable. It was extremely uncomfortable. In the body of the book, that which starts from the book's other side, I planned to make so, so many changes in the line-by-line text. Many times, when I was reading the book aloud at this or that bookstore, some word choice or passage appalled me to a point where I'd have to stop, mid-sentence, and furiously cross out the offending words, much to the amusement of the attendees, who thought I was kidding. The cause of the problem, in part, was the speed at which some of the book was written, and the difficulty I had in revising it. I didn't write it quickly because I wanted it written quickly. I wrote it quickly because, frankly, it was like writing, while drunk, in a sauna. Not drunk. On speed. Anxiety mixed with physical discomfort mixed with a faint warm and comfortable feeling, but tempered knowing that if I stayed too long in this place I would suffocate or bleed to death, after banging my fists and head against the humid wooden walls. It was at first warm and for a while the sweating felt good, but then some asshole kept putting water on those rocks, or whatever they do to make it hotter, and then I couldn't breathe, and I would flee the room where I was writing, and flee the book, and would dread, dread like one dreads seeing a bad-smelling distant elderly relative lying prone in a rank and wrong nursing home, going back to that time, to that book. I'm still amazed that I finished it in the first place, and am also surprised when I see some passages, because, frankly, there are sentences I wrote and never reread; there are pages I never looked at again. And the really problematic thing is that right now, I'm sitting here, in late September of 2000, and I have at this moment four days to finish whatever revisions I'd like to make, and I have been stalling on doing so for two months, for the same reason—because I really don't like being in that goddamned sauna, a sauna full of family and friends, at different ages, all looking at me curiously, all under the most clinical light. And I don't know if they hate me or love me or pity me, some combination thereof, or want to see me flayed and eaten by crows, or wish that I would just quietly go away. So the first chapter in particular will have almost no changes, because I just, a few minutes ago, tried to get in there, and after scrolling through the first half-page, I was already having trouble breathing. Now, twenty minutes later, I am still having trouble breathing. I hate being in that chapter again, in that brown low-ceilinged room. I can feel the air in that room of fake wood paneling, and smell those medicinal smells, can smell the bile, which has a smell, a robust scent, and I can see her eyes, and I didn't like her eyes that way, so tired and angry and yellowed and sunken, when they should be bright and angry and laughing and piercing and able to murder people and love people—exploding and infinite were her eyes!—and I don't want to feel the texture of that couch, that cheap synthetic velour, or walk around on that worn-through white wall-to-wall, or see the coffee table where my father put his sock feet, and I don't want to knock over a glass resting on the couch's sidetable, where he kept his death-bringing accoutrement, and I don't want to look out onto the driveway and hope no one pulls up in some stupid big car, bringing food they baked for us, or flowers, or wanting to come in and talk, the women with their fur and perfume, obscene, and I don't want to hide in the bathroom and look through the window over the toilet and see that fucking yard, the weeds closing in on the grass, year after year after year, no matter how much I cut that lawn the weeds moved in. And now, here in Brooklyn, I want to go outside, to the park maybe, but it's raining, and it's cold rain, and Toph's not home, so there would be nothing to do anyway so fuck it.

There won't be all that many changes after all. There are a few new passages in the main text, three to be exact, and they all involve Toph and me, and some things we did. Otherwise, as much as I felt I needed to, I've left my mistakes intact. The book was written by a 28-year-old person, and that 28-year-old person was trying to channel the thoughts he had when he was 21, 22, 23, 24, 25, 26 and 27. So I'm going to let all those people talk and act as they did, for better or worse.

d) *Many names have been changed.*

Yes, and I've taken out the phone numbers, too. Writing the first edition, I placed much weight on employing as many real names as possible, using their actual working phone numbers, everything, to prove a point that one could be completely factual, and still tell a story that felt and read novelistic, somewhat timeless, at least fluid. Changing all the names or, worse, making it all fictional (*semi*-autobiographical) seemed cowardly and silly. And so before publication, I approached people whose names were used, and asked their permission. All readily agreed, but now, many of the people who initially said yes have had second thoughts. A typical conversation before publication:

"Is it okay to use your real name?"

"Sure, why not?"

Typical conversation a month after publication:

"Would it be possible to remove my name?"

"Of course. Why?"

"Well, no offense, but I really didn't think anyone would see the damn book."

A slightly different thing happened with the three friends who allowed the usage of their phone numbers. [see page 215]. I assumed that after a few months, those whose numbers were listed would have been so besieged by creative teenagers at sleepovers that they'd have to change their numbers, a service I promised to pay for. And yet: approximate number of copies of this book sold in hardcover form: 200,000; approximate number of readers of this book, considering library use and pass-along: maybe 400,000; thus, how weird is this:

Number of calls Marny received: 7

Number of calls Kirsten received: 12

Total calls for K.C.: 5

Total number of calls: 24. Those that did call often hung up; those that spoke were very nice. But overall, a remarkable thing: a gaspingly low percentage of phoners, especially given just how easy and convenient telephone use can be. My guess is that a majority of people either a) assumed the numbers were phony or outdated; b) were exceedingly polite and respectful of the privacy of nonfictional book characters; or c) never actually made it that far into the book, a failure for which I cast no outward blame. The fault, of course, is mine.

But back to the idea of real people in books:

Most of the conversations, actually, were very similar. No one ever raised the slightest objection, and one person, now called Rebecca, was actually the first person to even ask to see the portion of the book in which she had a cameo. I asked why she thought this was, why she thought no one batted an eyelash, why people seemed not put off, but excited about the prospect.

"Maybe," she said, "it's a community kind of thing."

"Yeah," I said.

"Yeah," I said, believing it more the second time.

And this also informs why the character called John not only tolerated but actually sort of wanted his troubles documented: because secrets do not increase in value if kept in a Gore-ian lockbox, because one's past is either made useful or else mutates and becomes cancerous. So John figured what the fuck—he did some stupid things, and now he was moving on and, ostensibly, up. Further, it's like what was humbly suggested in Aspect D: THE TELLING THE WORLD OF SUFFERING AS MEANS OF FLUSHING OR AT LEAST DILUTING OF PAIN ASPECT. We share things for the obvious reasons: it makes us feel un-alone, it spreads the weight over a larger area, it holds the possibility of making our share lighter. And it can work either way—not simply as a pain-relief device, but, in the case of not bad news but good, as a share-the-happy-things-I've-seen/lessons-I've-learned vehicle. Or as a tool for simple connectivity for its own sake, a testing of waters, a stab at engagement with a mass of strangers—one or all of the above constitutes the motivation behind everyone with a personal ad, a website, a magazine, a radio show. All good.

Speaking of personal and often pathetic attempts at reaching: one of the things that mercifully isn't covered in the book is the author's truly iffy and semi-brief career as a cartoonist. For the entire time covered in the book, I was doing a weekly cartoon for *SF Weekly*, a newspaper published a few blocks from the *Might* offices. The cartoon, as *Might* did, sought to engage its readers, to provoke interaction, however glancing, and thus had an abiding curiosity in how people would react to solicitations placed within its clumsily rendered borders. Accordingly, one of its favorite experiments involved the giving away of the original artwork used in the cartoon, via the trunk of my car. At the time, after our Civic was crushed by the SUV en route to my sister's Kiss-featuring wedding, we bought a 1972 BMW 2002, a truly funny and perfect car, colored chartruese. And so I made an offer to the readers, that if they should see the car parked on any city street, that they should open the trunk, which would be unlocked always, and inside they would find drawings used in published cartoons. They could take a drawing, sign a register indicating who they were and what they took, and then they could go on their way, merrily. It worked. In a few weeks, all the artwork was gone, and everyone had signed their names, and it felt, I have to say, as if the lattice, described feebly on page 211, had grown, new and scraggly lines connecting dots always there. So then, drunk on trust, I started leaving not only the trunk open but all the cars' doors unlocked. And in about six months of this, never was anything stolen or the car otherwise molested, outside of the pollution littered under the car's windshield wipers by the city's vigilant and efficient and completely evil meter maids, venal and carniverous people in ridiculous helmets, may they and their overlords all burn in Hell eternally with much crackling and bubbling and searing of melted flesh—yes I will watch with glee, drooling on my silken-feathered wings.

What's weird is that, just as with the initial book that begins on the other side, I first thought the drawings-in-trunk would be a great idea—trust! community!—while often wondering if it was a terrible idea—theft! vandalism!—then figured I should turn back, then thought it was too late to turn back, then felt as if headed toward certain doom, then felt like, well, of course I *deserve* that certain doom, given my many sins, beginning with, when twelve, the use of the hand-held shower nozzle for self-pleasuring (many many years before even knowing what would result from even a few moments more of said self-pleasuring). The point is that trust is usually rewarded, even

though trust is sometimes violated, horribly. Trust is fun. It is fun to
trust strangers. It is fun to risk what you can reasonably risk—like,
your car, or your reputation—on the trust of people you know only
through something ephemeral shared, something like taste in books or
cartoons, or having watched people suffer. I still have this registry, and
have just decided to reproduce some of these names, along with their
entries in the column devoted to Hobbies. This will be done in small
type, and, like this appendix, can be ignored.

But why, then, have we changed most of the names in the book?
Because I've lost my taste for this sort of courage. I thought it was
courageous to write about these things, and I thought it was equally
courageous for my friends and I to use our names and phone numbers,
and to allow our exploits and sexploits to be recounted in print for the
consumption of our parents and aunts and nephews. But now, when so
many have asked for name-changes, and so many have been shocked by
who/how many have seen all these words, I've decided to let most of
the people—save some primary characters—breathe easier and live
freer, by allowing them to slip back into semi-fictional personae. It is
not my right to tell anyone else's story, and they don't owe me the favor
of allowing me to do so. In a few cases, where I had originally lashed
out at real people in backhanded ways, and used their real names in
doing so, I have removed or softened these parts, because in the last
year, I've also, almost completely, lost my taste for blood.

So, generally, the entries, no matter what their genre or origin,
whether they be addenda or corrections or clarifications, are all
arranged the same way, like so:

Page number of passage in question	Approximate location of passage, on the page (paragraph numbers exempt paragraphs begun on previous pages)	Either a) Words from book which will be corrected; b) Words from book that give rise to updates or clarifications; c) Tangential subject somehow related to passage cited
\	/	/

p. xi, paragraph 3: *Also removed was a fantastic scene*
We had been given a chance to try out, for free, a new
sportsman's tour—a kayak trip around Angel Island...

This should be clear enough. All entries may be skipped, or read
without attention to order. They are here for you, for your fun-having
and to be enjoyed at your convenience. Let's say, to shank a metaphor,

that this section is much like an absurdly colored car, parked on a thoroughfare, with its trunk open. Take what you want.

p. xi, paragraph 3: *Also removed was a fantastic scene—100 percent true—featuring most of the book's primary characters, and a whale.*

We had been given a chance to try out, for free, a new hearty tourist's tour—a kayak trip around Angel Island. It's hilly, heavily forested but, since the early 1900s—when it served as sort of a West Coast Ellis Island—an uninhabited and largely uneventful rock, dumped in the middle of San Francisco Bay. Asserting our freedom to leave the office on any day or at any time, four of us from work went at noon, took a ferry from Fisherman's Wharf and once at the island, we paired up: Marny and I in one kayak, Moodie and Zev in another. The guide, in a single-seater, rounded out the party, and we set out. The guide's name was not Bart, but we will be calling him Bart.

Ocean kayaking is very often very boring. Whereas whitewater kayaking has built-in interest, involving foam and speed enjoyed without having to self-generate that speed, ocean kayaking (which is essentially what a Bay kayak trip is) is akin to cross-country skiing—the pace is slow, the sights are unchanging and the work is tedious. And speed, really the only reason to partake in any sport, is almost impossible to achieve to any satisfactory degree.

The day was blue and yellow, and there was no wind. About halfway around the island, my shoulders already hurt like a mother; I was having some kind of rotator cuff problem. Naturally I thought of Jim McMahon and his own rotator cuff problems. Then thought of his headbands. And his part in "The Super Bowl Shuffle," the now-wildly underrated football anthem from 1984. Then of Walter Payton, easily one of the most graceful athletes in any sport ever, in whose body cancer was already taking root, growing, planning expansion, sprawling, though no one yet knew it.

Then.

There! About a thousand yards into the Bay, toward the city, a sudden plume of steam, coming from a shiny grey-black sliver rounded over the water's surface. A whale. *Fuck me, a whale*, someone said. Almost surely someone said that. Then it disappeared. Then someone said: *Holy shit*. Then: *Jesus fuck*.

We paddled furiously toward it, making our way to the site of breach, and when we got there, we waited. It was silly, really: we knew the whale was gone, so to look for it in the precise location it had appeared would assume that it was just bobbing in place, below us, which of course it was not. Whales do not bob in place; whales are on the *move*, whales have places to *go*. But still we waited, because we are dumb people who do dumb things.

It was bright. The city was white to our left, and the ocean was straight ahead, a few miles west. The water was still, and we rested our paddles on the kayaks. Our legs were underwater but dry. Our faces were getting burned. We took handfuls of the Bay's cold and wet our faces and our necks. We scanned the surface for a break.

Then: it came up again, this time about 500 yards toward the ocean. Same plume, same huge grey-black back breaking the surface, turning like a slow, dull bandsaw. *Goddamn*, someone said. Again we sped toward the location of its last appearance. Bart was excited. Bart had been kayaking in the Bay for years and years, and had never seen anything like this, a whale, in person, not 500 yards away.

We arrived where we had last seen it: nothing. We felt stupid again, but less stupid than before: maybe he, the whale, knew we were here, watching him; maybe our chasing him had induced his second appearance. Whales are smart, and if whales are smart, surely they enjoy these kinds of chasing games, as do all smart animals, like dogs, and dolphins, and many others I could name but will not, including those known as pigs, a kind of animal which everyone claims is smart, without any impressive behavioral evidence to back it up.

So we waited. Three, five minutes.

Then, into the Bay, again: the plume, the back, holy Jesus. A third appearance, this time 300 yards from its last. We didn't know what to do: follow it again? Just wait for the next breach? Wouldn't we have a better chance of a close-up visit if we stayed put? We decided to paddle halfway toward it, and then wait.

We did, and once there, we put our paddles down, exhausted. My rotator cuff ached. I thought of Jim McMahon again. And then of Jim McMahon's sunglasses, which were big, and wrapped around his head —in the early 80s, a new and mysterious thing. Who was he playing for now? Was he still so intriguingly rebellious? We were in the middle of the Bay, a few inches out of the water, on a blue and yellow day, and we were chasing a whale. We looked at each other and grinned. But we were tired. We were tired, and were thinking that we really should get moving, toward the beach, where we planned to have our lunch. The beach looked inviting. On the beach we would see our legs again, and be able to walk using these legs, which were at the moment underwater, immobile; this pose can be unsettling after a while.

We were arranged like this:

Direction of last sighting of whale

Again we waited. This time about ten minutes. We were content, because we were tired, and because we were already satisfied, having seen a whale, while kayaking, in the Bay, near our homes, in our city, on a clear day while we were young.

Now. See the "x"?

That's where the motherfucker came up.

He surfaced right between us. Not three feet away from our kayak. Much closer to Bart's. More than close. It was under Bart's kayak, not just under it but under it in such a way that when it surfaced, Bart's kayak was *on top of the whale*. It scared the piss out of us. I yelped. Everyone else made more civilized sounds. Gasps. I thought the whale might eat us.

Then Bart, God bless him, while he was being lifted from the water by this forty-foot monster, had the presence of mind to *reach down and touch it*. The whale—God, thinking about it now, it seems like it was there, between us all, for *hours*—it had this big dull eye, and the eye was looking at us, and the whale's whole back was bumped and barnacled, a thousand years old, and his mouth could have crushed us all, toothless though, the thing hardly an animal and more like a huge rough rock, a big rubbery rock rolling under us—

And then it sunk from under Bart's kayak, setting the kayak's shiny fiberglass bottom back upon the surface, and in a second it was gone.

And right then, if I was ever unsure of it before, I was certain that we had been marked. When a whale surfaces between your kayaks—

chooses, among any of 2 or 3 million places in a Bay to breach, chooses a spot between your tiny plastic kayaks—this giant ancient creature, who very well might be some kind of alien, a billion years old and maybe the creator of the whole world and everything in it (why not?), has come from the blue-grey depths to terrify you—that means everything is possible. No one can need more proof than that.

p. xxii: *Offer of digital version in exchange for whole book*
Number of people who actually sent in books to be exchanged for disc bearing digital version of book: 4. Number of discs sent to these people, as of presstime: 0. (I will get to it soon, I promise.)

p. xxii: *Offer of $5 rebate*
I've gotten about 1,000 letters (I actually have no idea how many letters have been sent, but it seems like a 1,000. Could be 250.) but the very shockingly nice thing is that almost all of them, if they mentioned the rebate at all, said the same thing: Don't worry about the money, I just wanted to say hi. Which is nice, being said hi to.

p. xxxiv, paragraph 3: *THE MEMOIR AS SELF-DESTRUCTION ASPECT*
This Aspect turned out to be much too prescient. See, the Acknowledgments were written before the rest of the book, as both an organizational device and a stalling mechanism. I was not looking forward to writing the first chapter, and wasn't sure if I could write those thereafter, so I had a nice time fiddling with the front matter, which came easily, and helped me to shape the book in my head before starting into it. This Aspect, though, was probably the most crucial, in that I truly felt while writing the book that actually publishing it would be the end of me. I thought that a) the book would alienate me from my friends and relatives, even those who had read it well before publication and provided approval; and b) the book would enrage many readers for one reason or another, and would compel them to come and kill me. In October of 1998, when I started working in earnest on finishing the book's original text, and was poring through hundreds of journal entries, I called my brother Bill at about 4 a.m. one night and talked into his machine for a while about what should happen to these entries should I get hit by a train or blown up in an airplane or, most likely, killed by a man in an elevator, wearing a trenchcoat. (For years I feared the opening of every elevator, half-convinced that from the opened doors would come a bullet, for

me, shot by a man in a tan trenchcoat. I have no idea why I feared this, expected it to happen. I even knew how I would react to this bullet coming from the elevator door, what word I would say. That word was: *Finally*.) So I told Bill not to worry, that I was not suicidal, never that— when we leave such messages, we always have to render the boundaries immediately, so as not to provoke worry—but that, should anything happen, that under no circumstances was anyone to be allowed to see any of my journal entries, that even if behavioral scientists begged for them, that he was not to release them, and under no circumstances was he to compile any unfinished stuff, edit it without mercy and make it into a book about a safari-oriented *ménage à trois*. The call to Bill reflected both my usual death-paranoia and also the fact that around that time the creation of the book began to seem eerily like a coming, self-induced death, probably a violent one. As if I'd been diagnosed with something horrible, something quick and unmerciful, ebola maybe, and that I was heading toward its inevitable result with no options other than to allow it to eat me from the inside out, liquify my innards—or else take matters into my own hands and beat the ebola to the punch. I began to wonder why there are so many symptomatic similarities between the way I was thinking, and the way I'd read that suicidal people feel. I woke up late each day, I showered occasionally, I did not clean my house— Yes, none of these things were new, but other things were. Chiefly, when I thought about suicide, it no longer seemed like such a foreign concept, such a remote possibility. Not that I've ever had any active suicidal thoughts—I've been shown, by my brain's 24-hour worst-case-scenario cable channel, passive thoughts, of course, as is my curse—but at this point I did start to frequently, unintentionally envision the event. The impulse toward suicide began to seem like something that could creep up on me, something that was more plausible than before, and something that might seem increasingly plausible in the future. I was tired, and my water-treading abilities seemed to be weakening. Then of course there was the likelihood, more glamorous and self-serving for someone begotten by a Catholic martyr, that someone would kill me, as I kept picturing. And oddly enough, when not picturing it happening from the cavity of a closing elevator, I envisioned it occuring, fittingly enough, at a reading. In one of my many such daydreams, there was a recurring image of a man in a raincoat pushing through the assembled with a snub-nosed pistol and, once close enough, shooting me square in the chest. In the scenario, which was for some reason always set in the back portion of Rose Records, a music-purveying shop on Green Street in Champaign, Illinois, I always vaccilate between a) jumping under the desk and avoiding the shots long enough for him to be wrestled to the ground by... by bookstore security, I guess; and b) the reaction that seems to make more sense: I sit up straight and offer my chest to him, take the bullet, and am killed. [Interesting side note to this tangent based on a clarification: As I have been writing and revising this book (*this part written in June of 1999*), I was just sitting here, working on another section, actually, when I had another vision of my being shot while at a table signing books. This time, I was at A Clean Well Lighted Place for Books, on Van Ness Street in San Francisco, and for some reason the vision was from the point of view of someone in line to have me sign a book. So I was standing there, a witness this time, and just glimpsed, ahead of me about fifteen feet, a sudden movement, a boom, and then a flailing of the person at the desk with the books, who was, of course, me.] So because I knew that many people would be saddened by the appearance of this book—those who cared about my father, for instance, and feel I was unfair—I figured that after its publication, I'd be in hiding somewhere, that I would disappear—to safety! Right. So, the visions and their increased dream-to-life probability brought to mind what I used to tell Toph, when he would come to me when he couldn't sleep, when he was terrified, as I was, at age 9, of death, not of imminent death but any death at all, eventual death, the prospect of death, the fact of death somehow more tangible at 9 than at 30 or 50—he, like I did at his age, saw the door of life closing already, however distantly and slowly, and couldn't bring himself to sleep, and so, sitting on the couch in our place in Berkeley, we had to talk about the afterlife, and my explanation to him at that point was this: "Well, Toph, I do believe in some sort of afterlife, I suppose because it just seems more logical that there is one than there is not. I mean, if we can so clearly conceive of it, if so many disparate (no, I didn't use that word at the time) peoples can conceive of it, then it almost means that there must be..." Etc. And that's how I had come to think about imminent and violent death, the shot from the man in the elevator or at the reading: because I saw it so often, and it was beginning to make more and more sense, to seem less and less fantastical and more logical and mundane, then it almost followed that it was more likely than before, that it had been preordained, mapped out more or less, given a time frame, scheduled, and I had been simply watching previews of something coming, without equivocation, soon.

Much later, while finishing the book, in the fall of 1999, I found myself walking around my Brooklyn neighborhood in the middle of the night, on my way to buy more caffeine, involuntarily chanting things to myself, in a whisper. Things like:

Mistake mistake mistake mistake mistake mistake mistake

Or:

Oh fuck Oh fuck Oh fuck Oh fuck Oh fuck Oh fuck
Oh fuck Oh fuck Oh fuck Oh fuck

Or slightly more complex, like say:

Oh Jesus give me give me Oh Jesus give me give me Help help no no
Jesus no no no no no Help Jesus no no

Or one that went something like:

To die, will die, to die, will die, don't know, to die, will die,
don't know, will die, don't know, who who who who WHO?

I never really knew where the chants came from, because I would find myself doing them without consciously choosing their words. And then, after having whispered the words feverishly for blocks without really noticing, I would catch myself and then try to stop, which was usually easy but sometimes not so easy, in a way that reminded me a lot of shivering, much like how you shiver in weather that does not completely demand shivering: to quell the shivering or shaking or teeth-chattering—I learned this in the Chicago winters, when we would go to the lake and invariably drop a foot through the ice—you put your mind and lungs to it, and with enough concentration you can slow your breathing, relax your body and quit shivering, in part because you've also convinced your brain that there is no reason to be shivering, it being not quite cold enough to warrant it. Likewise, you can usually squelch the mantras of doubt and doom that bring whispers to your lips when you're walking around your neighborhood, black and blue in the small hours, and quiet. So. Either way, the words would invariably stop once I opened the front door to my apartment. Actually, before I forget, among the many chants—again, completely subconsciously formed—this was the most prevalent:

Sorry sorry sorry Oh God sorry sorry sorry Oh God sorry sorry sorry sorry
Sorry sorry sorry sorry sorry sorry sorry sorry Oh God

The involuntary chanting could have been symptomatic of two results of the writing of the book, alluded to in this ASPECT we're discussing.

To wit:

1) There is the need, in many people who feel guilt about outliving someone they love, to punish themselves in any way possible, and who vaguely dream of their own death, often a slow and painful death like those who died before them, a death that they feel will purify them and absolve them of the sin of living on. And:

2) There is, intrinsic to the process of a memoir, the resulting destruction of one's former self. Writing about those years, and being as cruel to who I was as I could be implicitly means that you are killing that person. Yes, you are sometimes celebrating that person's better moments, and relating with sympathy that person's better thoughts, but overall you are saying: This was me then, and I can look at that person, from the distance I now have, and throw water balloons on his stupid fat head. But even as good an idea as that seems to be, an idea attractive to the intellectually violent, it is also a very painful plan to carry out, and one that is rebelled against, by various self-preservative internal forces. Which is not to say anything of what happens once those thoughts are read and processed by the public at large. However much I tried to make happen the things I wanted to happen, and however much I tried to prevent things from happening that I hoped would not, they happened anyway. It was, for the most part, very entertaining. Were parts of the process incredibly painful? They were. I wrote a book in large part about the deaths of my parents, and living with my brother thereafter, and this, inexplicably, brought out in a very few people a kind of malice that I have rarely seen. Very strange. But it was not entirely unexpected. The weird thing is that while writing the original text, I had in my head not the usual Writer's Ideal Reader, but instead my own potential reading person, the Mean/Jaded/ Skimming Reader—the person I had been for many years. Thus I expected the worst from the book's readers, I expected claws and blood and teeth. The book ends with a plea for those who would tear into me to just go ahead and do it, because I wanted it to happen, finally. But then a weird thing happened: People were kind. It was almost impossible to find people who were as vicious and small as I had for many years been. Not completely impossible, but still: I expected crucifixion and instead got something more like its opposite. More about this later.

p. xlv, paragraph 1: *$100 to John Warner*
I never actually gave John Warner his $100. I have no good explanation
for why I did not. John, I am sorry. But rest assured that the size of your
wedding gift will reflect the amount owed.

p. 1, paragraph 3: *On using the word Mother when I probably should have used
the word Mom*
I had never, before writing the book, even once used the word Mother
when talking to or about my mom (Mom). In all contexts she was Mom,
or a mom—never Mother, or a mother, a word formal or severe and thus
unfitting. But in print, the word *Mom* strangely triples its informality,
and becomes fey. We need a new word. *Moth? Momther? Mothem?* I'm
open to suggestions, care of this publisher.

p. 3, paragraph 1: *The half-moon container*
The exact look of this container, the half-moon container, was, while
writing, relatively fuzzy in my head. That is to say, I remember it fair-
ly well, but never asked Beth or Bill specifically if my recollection was
correct, nor did I visit a hospital to see if such things, described as I had,
in fact existed. It was one of the details, and there were a few of them,
where I would not have been at all surprised to hear that I was very far
off. About six months ago, I was looking through boxes, which I often
do knowing I'll find something horrible or wonderful and the next
hours would either explode or melt or break open, and I found this container. I don't remember saving it, and doubt Beth would have saved it,
but there it was, in perfect condition. It was and still is plum-colored,
but is not actually half-moon-shaped. It is in the shape of a crescent
moon, a one-quarter moon, a circle's first turn—the mouth of a smiling
face on a sticker encouraging personal contentment.

p. 4, paragraph 2: *Television programming during nosebleed episode*
All shows described were watched at one time or another with my mom,
but maybe (or probably) not on all that day. She did love *Studs,* though.

p. 7, paragraph 3: *Video games*
This is a very oblique reference to the fact that my dad played video
games, from Pong to Atari to Colecovision to Nintendo, consistently

and with great gusto. Every night, after watching a full night's worth of the networks' offerings, and then the news, he would enlist one of us, usually me, and I would be sent to the back of the TV to switch the lever from TV to Videogame, and he would pull the two controllers from under the coffee table, put in a cartridge, and the beating would begin. He was not good. Any of us could beat him at any game at all, no matter how long he had been practicing. (He often practiced in preparation.) He was never good, really. He was not good at Pong, and was not good at Breakout, or Frogger, or QBert, or Championship Golf, or Donkey Kong, or the original Legend of Zelda. But it was interesting to watch him try, and it also made Christmas more promising, given that he wanted new games or new systems as much or more than the rest of us. I wanted to relate this about him, because he had a very large appetite for fun, a love of long narrative jokes involving Stosh and John, too bumbling fishermen of Polish descent, and he loved to watch *Monty Python,* and *The Muppet Show,* and *The Simpsons.* And he played pool. And when he played pool, in the storeroom in the basement, I was allowed to watch, and sometimes to play, though his frustration about my still-improving technique and results was unwavering. I would follow him downstairs, past the main basement playroom, and into the darker storeroom, full of boxes and the pool table and the crawlspace where the bodies likely were. He would pull the string to the light over the table, and it and the light would swing to and fro while he found his cue and chalked its tip, a function he performed with quick but careful [weird: as I was writing that last sentence, I looked briefly out the window, trying to think of the right words for how he chalked his cue, and from the huge pine tree near my window came a small bird, flying toward me. When he flew within about six feet of hitting my window I had a sudden suspicion that he was my father, and he was trying to tell me to stop writing about his pool playing. Then, just before the bird flew into the window, he swept up and over the roof.] He played straight pool. He thought eight-ball was a loser's game, and so we counted balls, keeping score on the abacus-looking device hung near the boiler. He had a good break, and a soft touch, and scorned the use of the bridge for far-away shots. That would be too easy.

p. 8, paragraph 4: *Elms in front yard*
I can't be sure that they were elms. Elms sounds right. They might have

been oaks. Or one elm, and one oak. Or all maples—it's hard to say. See, our yard, when we moved in as toddlers, started with about six huge trees in the front yard, next to the driveway. But as we grew, it seemed that every year a different tree would die—we never knew how one could tell that it was or wasn't dead; all we understood was that at some point tree-expert men would come to chop it down. Of course, we never actually saw it being done, the tree removal, and the only reason I can think or hope that this was so was that my parents made sure the cutting down of the trees was done while we were gone at school, them wanting to avoid, I guess, the traumatic effects the tree removal might have on our young tree-loving dispositions. So we would come back from school, on our banana-seated bicycles, ride down Oakdale—you could really get going pretty fast on Oakdale, past the house where Ed and Ted and Fred Liu lived—and on onto and across our street, Waveland, then jump the lip on our driveway and then suddenly notice something different about the yard, something hard to pinpoint at first, and then *Oh!* there would just be *That's it!* this clean, flat-topped stump on the lawn. Not that it was always obvious that there was a tree missing; it was, actually, rarely obvious. It was more like an addition than a subtraction. Then we'd drop our bikes and would jump on the stump for a while, pick through it for bugs and worms, and then, shortly thereafter, the stump would be made into a base for kickball.

p. 10, paragraph 8: *Wondering what fishwater tastes like*
I don't remember specifically wondering what the water in the fish tank would taste like. It's the sort of thing I might have imagined, but not something I remember actually doing. I was just writing about the room, and while writing about it, and the fish tank, I was wondering, just as any American would have done if placed in my shoes, what it would have tasted like. Maybe we'll never know.

p. 32, paragraph 6: *Mittens*
Not sure if Toph was actually wearing mittens.

p. 43, paragraph 1: *Pachelbel*
I have talked about the Persistence of Poignance. Try this one on for size: Just tonight, on New Year's Eve, 1998/9, Toph and I had nothing much to do. I had considered going out and leaving him alone, he being

15 and all, then considered bringing him to parties in the city, then realized I didn't really care much about parties in the city, and it was so, so cold, so we rented a VCR and three movies and ordered Chinese food—crispy chicken and lemon chicken, both with sauces on the side; $15.20, plus tip. Let me back up for a second, because this is where the poignance part comes in: we were at the video store, and I was looking at the new releases, trying not to stare at the cover of *Blame It on Rio*, the movie that I secretly wanted to rent, desperately, actually, when a box came into my vision: *Ordinary People*. Toph, having almost no knowledge of the Judith Guest book and only vaguely knowing what the book/movie means in terms of where we once lived, etc., suggested we rent it; I have no idea why. I readily agreed, not having seen the movie in years, and so we went home and I was so anxious I couldn't get the thing in the rented VCR quickly enough, actually, and as the opening credits rolled, I realized that, yes, Pachelbel's Canon in D is the music running throughout. I mean, how sick or predictable or just strange are we? The music is in *Ordinary People*, a movie about untimely death in Lake Forest, so we play the music ourselves, in our house as—

A few weeks later I called my sister:

"Beth, why did you play that music?"

"I don't remember playing that music."

And this is the way things are.

p. 58, paragraph 14: *Johnny Bench*

Johnny Bench: Toph insists that there is no way he wouldn't have known who Johnny Bench was. He suggests that I should have used someone more obscure, like Jody Davis, also a catcher (Cubs, mid-eighties), who as we all know predated Joe Girardi (Cubs, later Yankees), who visited his class in second grade, much to the amazement of the school's tiny people, because his wife, Girardi's, taught, for a time, at Cherokee Elementary, my school, Toph's school, a very good school.

p. 71, paragraph 1: *General chronology in domestic chapter*

It may have been obvious, but many of the events described, where Toph and I are at home, messing around, all that, did not actually take place in one night. That's not to say that there were not countless nights that actually did include that much fun and frivolity (or more!). It's just that it's unlikely that there was a night composed of specifically those events.

For instance, on that day, we might have been doing laundry, folding it on my bed, with him afterward taking his pile up to his room, where he would deposit the appropriate items in the appropriate drawers, the drawers squeaking open then thundering closed, the handles click-click-clicking afterward. Or it might have been the day he and his charming friend Ross, who was raised in this country but spoke with a British accent, established not a Lemonade Stand but instead a Smore's Stand, which worked like this: Ross, at the corner of Gilman and Peralta, would hold a sign up to passing cars, advertising the availability of these Smores. When a car would stop, he would yell down the block, six houses down, to Toph, who was standing on our driveway and when given the order, would run up the steps and into our house, sweep into the kitchen and to the microwave, which already housed a fully-constructed but not yet melted Smore, and would hit the Start button. After sixty seconds of bouncing impatiently and watching the progress through the microwave window, the beep would go and he'd pop open the door, deposit the treat onto a paper towel on his hand, and then slide through the living room, out the door, jump from the steps, down the block, and then would meet Ross halfway, hand off to him the hot merchandise, whereupon Ross would complete the run, to the waiting car.

p. 78, paragraph 1: *Simplification of Berkeley*
I simplified the Berkeley years quite a bit, in the interest of moving things along. A few important points: First, the one house described is actually an amalgam of two. We lived one year in one house, and at the end of the year, our landlord, she with the widening eyes, asked us to vacate, citing her need to sell the building. At which point we heard, kind of magically, of a vacancy across the street and three houses down. We begged for and got that place, which was bigger and better, cleaner, and moved in and stayed there for two years, while the owners were in Martinique. Both houses had roughly the same floor plans, so the diagram included on page 78 would work, more or less, for either. It should be noted that though we lived alone in the first house, when we moved to the second, the rent was higher, and we needed help, and so were joined by Flagg, a close grade-school friend, who had just moved out from Washington, D.C., and who we persuaded to share the rent, even though he'd have to commute to San Francisco. He lived with us for a year, sleeping in the front bedroom, between my room and Toph's. He

was not around all that much—he would stay in the city/The City many weekends—but when we were all together, all at home at the same time, it was grand, it was good, it was completely fucking great. Flagg had been Toph's first friend, and for probably the first five years of his speaking life, he cited *Fragg*, a teenager at the time, as his best friend. So in Berkeley, when we were all together, hitting each other with whiffle bats or wrestling on the kitchen floor and pinning Toph down to stuff bananas in his ears, or having him jump on his bed so we could knock his legs out from under him as he hit full height, I wondered how we would do without Flagg if he ever left. As much as I was trying to entertain Toph, Flagg was trying to entertain me, and us together, and it really got to the point where it was almost too much, too much good, a house where nothing productive could be done when we were all home. Squirtguns became a problem. Basketball was constant. Down the road and through the backyard of the gnome house, and to the little hidden park, we would play 21, pretty much the only game possible with three people. Or sometimes Horse. Flagg would always win any game, unless he decided to allow one of us to win, which he often did, or if he decided, instead of playing for real, to stand, off to one side, and, just before any shot, to throw off the shooter, stage-whisper: *"Ain't it a crime!"* This is what he did all the time. *"Ain't it a crime!"* And it had to be said in a hiss, sudden, while shaking one's head. We would start to shoot, would almost be letting the ball go when the hiss would come: *"Ain't it a crime!"* The phrase and delivery comes from an E. Murphy/J. Piscopo skit, c. 1984, wherein the two play detectives with an elite unit—the New Jersey Vice. They wore colorful suits and pastel T-shirts beneath, and solved crimes committed, almost exclusively, at the docks at midnight or the junkyard at dawn. So after seeing something gruesome, Eddie would chicken-jerk his head toward Piscopo and with alarmed eyes say the words: *"Ain't it a crime!"* It was unclear what this meant then, and it's still vague now. Much more mysterious is whence came the power of this phrase to make us miss shots. Flagg would say these words and we would lose all control of our limbs; the ball would fall from our hands and we would keel over. *"Ain't it a crime!"* We would die. *"Ain't it a crime!"* Why is that funny? *"Ain't it a crime!"* I'm sure everything's lost in the translation. *"Ain't it a crime!"* Toph could not stop giggling. And he never even *seen* the original show. *"Ain't it a crime!"* Is it funny when if I keep throwing it at you? *"Ain't it a crime!"* It's not funny. *"Ain't it a crime!"* It makes no sense.

After a year, Flagg moved out, understandably wanting to be closer to his job, and to people our age, though he was never all that far away. He came back often, and called often, sometimes asking for Toph, and when Toph got on the phone, the big phone around his little face, through the receiver came the whispered words: *"Ain't it a crime!"*

p. 84, paragraph 3: *Hat smelling like urine*
Toph insists, to this day, that his hat never smelled like urine. His claim is that it smelled like something else.
    "Like what?"
    "Like sweat."
    "It didn't smell like sweat."
    "It didn't smell like urine."
    "Why would I make that up?"
    "Because you're a freak."

p. 102, paragraph 4: *Free haircut*
We didn't actually get a free haircut. We insisted on paying then, as we insisted on paying always, because we had the money. She did offer, though. The barber shop was called Fred's, and is still there, on Deerpath Road, right in the middle of town.

p. 111, paragraph 2: *Purple beret*
This in a letter, received in late September 2000, from the purported beret-wearer: "Yes, it was in the purple family (though I would prefer 'raspberry'), but definitely *not a beret*. And it was a passing fancy that lasted only slightly longer than our 'relationship.' Just to clarify, an illustration is included for your edification." The letter was accompanied by three (let's be frank, primitive) drawings of what appears to be a duck. One duck is wearing what resembles a deflated football, and bears the caption: "Beret: rigid, upright, fitted jauntily to one side, very French, almost baguette-looking." The next drawing features the same duck, who suddenly has long hair, wearing something looking very much like a skullcap. The caption: "Soft cloche-like hat (almost cardinal/medieval in look; not at all French. More, say, 16th c. Spain)." The third drawing features

a back view of the duck in the second type of headwear, though the hair is rendered scraggly and random, when in actuality her hair is smooth and yellow and as generous as she, herself, this person who was improperly given a beret, is. Also, she does not look, at all, really, like a duck.

p. 134, paragraph 10: *Where is your brother?*
This happened: At a reading in Portland, I read the passage involving the being-annoyed-at-being-asked this question part, and, immediately afterward, a middle-aged woman in the third row raised her hand and asked, in English but with what sounded like a German accent: *So where iz ya brotdha now?* And she was not kidding. This sort of thing still happens. For fun, Toph and I actually did one reading together, in Austin, which turned out to be sort of a mistake, given the pleasure he takes in dismantling his brother's tendencies toward the precious. Sitting next to me, pen in hand, every page I would sign, he would turn over and, on its underside, go to work on a deconstruction or outright parody of whatever I had written in whomever's book. Below, an example.

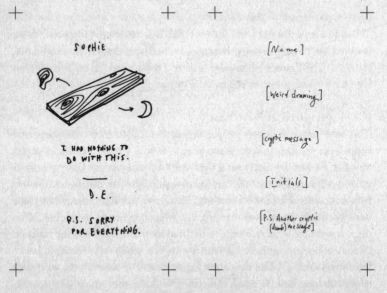

p. 138, paragraph 1: *Gun-to-school fake ha has.*
This conversation is printed almost verbatim, or as close to verbatim as possible, considering that Jenna and I had both been celebrating, it

being New Year's Eve, and we being in the backseat of a car traveling around San Francisco, looking for the third of four parties attended that night. Yes, I moved an event from New Year's Eve to the random night described, which would seem kind of backwards, I realize, in terms of how meaningful it might be to have had that conversation on the eve of a new year, not to mention the eve of my mother's birthday. Also: Dave Moodie was in the car, but was not paying attention. Had he heard it, and given his ability to crush my sternum when was his wont, I might not be sitting here today, writing this gorgeous prose.

p. 188, paragraph 1: *Young swastika-etchers*
Bill says that the young man who used to draw swastikas did not do so on the back of a bus seat, but in a *notebook*, while riding *on* the bus.

p. 192, paragraph 3: *Steve the Black Guy*
My older brother Bill, who was one year ahead of my sister Beth in high school, does not remember this Steve fellow being known as Steve the Black Guy. The story comes from Beth, who told it often, to me and to friends and acquaintences and, as is her habit, to strangers. That Bill didn't know of the moniker means only that, contrary to what I wrote, it's likely that Steve was not known school-wide as Steve the Black Guy, but rather was known as such by some smaller portion of the school, which included my sister Beth.

p. 211, paragraph 1: *Lattice*
Because we honestly did want people banding together. For me and I think for the rest of the coterie, what was important first was the alliance. An agenda, if we needed one, would come later. The warmth of other people, their electricity, then the direction of that energy somewhere, if need be. Does that make sense? How about this: True community cannot be political.

p. 225, paragraph 3: *About having never dreamt of my parents*
On January 14, 1999, I did. I was lying on the couch, and for no reason whatsoever I dozed off while stalling when I should have been working. I had a dream, and then, maybe seven hours later, writing at about 5:30 a.m., I was losing my mind. Not only because of the dream, but because, Jesus, January 14 was the day my mother died. Worst of all, as

I was writing about the dream, a song came over the stereo, unannounced, that featured, almost exclusively, bloodcurdling screams. The screams were on an album that I thought I knew well, but then, at the end, was simply a man screaming, his screams alternating with loud thumps, like a heavy object hitting an anvil. And each time it thumped I whipped my head around to see if she was there, expecting her to look not kind and motherly but tattered, wild-haired and murderous. The dream involved her coming toward me and [

[UNSETTLING PORTION DELETED FOR SAKE OF SANITY OF ALL]

                                                                          ]   This
was something strange and wrong, something she never would have done in life. I will say that the dream did contain a nice part where I was in our old kitchen and Toph was there, albeit at about 6 or 7 years old. His face was an amalgam of his at 5 and 6, while his body was taller, and I immediately realized, while in the dream, that I was being given this gift, being able to be with him again, at this age. We stood in the kitchen and I held his shoulders in front of me to get a look at him, with him allowing me, indulging me, though with his head down. He knows the moment means a lot to me. I hug him, pushing his head into my chest, and in the glass of the kitchen's sliding door, I notice that it's night and I can see our reflection in the glass. I gauge how tall he is, and make a note to remember this, that it will be a good detail to remember once the dream is over. (In the dream, I know that I am a tourist, that I am passing through.) I commit to memory that my chin comes to his eye, and soak in his soft hair, his little pudgy face, and I hold him against me.

And I woke up wanting to have babies.

p. 231, paragraph 1: *Forest-photo wallpaper*
On the swim team and diving team I swam and dove with a boy named Jonathan Joosten. He was compact and strong, and was the best diver we had, even though he was not of diver build or diver sensibility. You expect a lithe and possibly effete boy, one who might blow his bangs from his forehead by pushing outward his lower lip and emitting a thrust of steam upward through hair. But Joosten was stout and messy, practiced in a big sloppy T-shirt and couldn't have been more cavalier about his talent. He could do a double flip and finish perfectly, he could

do one-and-a-halfs from the side of the pool. He was good friends with Jeff Farlander, who of course we know from other parts of the book.

Jonathan's mother was a laconic and funny woman, divorced and merrily world-weary. She was an actress, and so took odd jobs to make ends meet. I found this out when one day I came home to find her in my bedroom, hanging wallpaper. The orange forest-scene wallpaper my mom and I had picked out was being applied to the wall, strip by strip, by Jonathan Joosten's mom. It was, for me, a bizarre occasion on a number of levels. First, I couldn't remember any adults besides my mom ever setting foot in my room. Even my father, whose threshold-crossing, I think, is the one described in the book. So this woman, who I had seen only at swim meets, was in my room, and why was this woman installing my wallpaper when men in overalls were supposed to be doing this kind of thing? I couldn't watch. I went to a friend's house while she did the work. I came back and she was gone and the forest was up and it was perfect.

The next year we quit the club—there is some debate whether we could no longer afford it, or whether we just quit. Over the years we would see Mrs. Joosten in a commercial every so often. She was the only actress we knew, the only person we had ever known who had been on TV, and so we worshiped her. The main ad we knew, because it was in heavy rotation for what seemed like years, was for the Illinois lottery. In it she played a waitress who forgot to play her numbers one day and thus missed out on, presumably, millions and the new and happy life attendant. They are in a diner, the two waitresses.

"Hey Miss Moneybags," says her coworker, "I see your number won."

Mrs. Joosten, coffee pot in hand, her dawning regret allowing it to tilt. With the most tangible existential sadness, the words sung but sung as the last sorrowful notes of a dying chanteuse, she says:

"I forgot to play."

Now. I'm writing this in July of 2000, in a cottage in Hvalsfjordur, an hour north of Reykjavík in Iceland, where Toph and I are spending a quiet month overlooking a blue-grey fjord and surrounded by sheep. There is a TV in the cottage, but it gets one channel only, and this one channel broadcasts only a few hours a day. They air a not-terrible mix of American, British and German shows, from *Veronica's Closet* to a German action show called *HeliCops*. The one boon is *The West Wing,* which airs

once a week, and around which we plan our evening. We cook dinner—
hamburgers or pizza is all that's edible here, we who hate fish—so that
it will be ready just as the show begins.

Tonight we've gotten dinner ready, and are sitting down, when
there is a knock on the door, and it's a man in his thirties, in overalls
and flannel shirt, flanked by his wife, who is holding their little girl,
who looks about four. They have come, they say in caveman English, to
cut the lawn. I remember the farmer's wife, from whom we're renting,
telling me something about this. But during *The West Wing*? I say fine,
fine, and close the door, hoping it won't be too loud.

It is loud, but we turn up the volume and are fine. While the mother and father cut the grass using gas-powered trimmers (not mowers),
their daughter plays on our porch, running to and fro, the sounds of hol-
low wood-plank-thumping. She's a typically cute blond Icelandic tiny
thing, in a bright red mini-parka, well-worn, and her parents are cutting lawns for money, so I hold none of her or their noise against them.
In fact, I get an idea. Because we are leaving the country in a few days
to return for some indefensible reason to New York City in August, I
get up during a commercial, empty the fridge and cabinets of their per-
ishables and other foodstuffs we can't eat before leaving, and put it all
in a grocery bag. I have it in my head that before this family leaves I will
present it to them, and they will be thankful, and they will think good
things about Americans, and in particular, about us.

But as I'm tying the grocery bag, I see the dad, lawn-trimming
with a cigarette dangling from his mouth. Fuck! I look at the girl and
feel awful for her. A smoking parent. Then, in a bizarrely well-timed
quick-cut, I see the mother, who inexplicably also has a cigarette in her
mouth, while also trimming the lawn. They are a dual-parent-smoking
family, and suddenly I hate them. I put the entire grocery bag in the
fridge; they won't get any of it. I briefly wonder if I should be punish-
ing the child for the sins of her parents, then decide that the parents
need to be punished, by me and others, until such time as they cease
smoking period or at least in front of their young child with her young
delicate lungs and throat, so that the girl does not grow up deep-down
enraged about her parents' overt but slow suicide and become judg-
mental and cruel, and with access to a word processor.

The commercial was over and *The West Wing* returned.

The point of the story, and its connection to Jonathan Joosten, is this: in the middle of tonight's episode, which I think is the season finale, Martin Sheen, as the president, walks out of his office and says something to a woman, an older-secretaryish woman, who says something back, barbed. This woman, I think, looks familiar. Then I become increasingly sure that the woman playing President Sheen's secretary is the very same woman who installed my wallpaper, the wallpaper into which I wanted so badly, that night and other nights, to run. I wait for the credits, and I am right: *Also starring Kathryn Joosten.* The woman who installed my forest-scene wallpaper is now the secretary to the too-good-for-dreams president of the United States.

I tell Toph—who did, after all, grow up in the same bedroom, with the same wallpaper—and he is mildly interested. Then I hear the start of a car, and see the family, probably doomed, pulling out of the driveway, and I watch them skid and bounce down the dirt road toward the water, past the sheep who stand alert.

p. 235 to 237, and in general all over: *Irony and its Malcontents*

This section should be skipped by most, for it is annoying and pedantic, and directed to a very few. They know who they are. Here we go: You can't know how much it pains me to even have that word, the one beginning with *i* and ending in *y*, in this book. It is not a word I like to see, anywhere, much less type onto my own pages. It is beyond a doubt the most over-used and under-understood word we currently have. I have that *i*-word here only to make clear what was clear to, by my estimations, about 99.9% of original hardcover readers of this book: that there is almost no irony, whatsoever, within its covers. But to hear a few people tell it, this entire book, or most of it, was/is ironic. Well. Well. Ahem. Well. Let's define irony as the dictionary does: *the use of words to express something different from and often opposite to their literal meaning.* (There are lesser definitions, but they all serve this main one.) Now, where, keeping that definition in mind, do we find that herein? We do find some things that might have confused the reader prone to presuming this irony, so let's address them one at a time: 1. When someone *kids around*, it does not necessarily mean he or she is being *ironic*. That is, when one tells a joke, in any context, it can mean, simply, that *a joke is being told*. Jokes, thus, do not have to be *ironic* to be *jokes*. Further, *satire* is not inherently *ironic*. Nor is *parody*. Or any kind of *comedy*. Irony is a very specific and not all that interesting thing, and to use the word/concept to blanket half of all contemporary cultural production—which some agéd arbiters seem to be doing (particularly with regard to work made by those under a certain age)—is akin to the too-common citing of "the Midwest" as the regional impediment to all national social progress (when we all know the "Midwest" is ten miles outside of any city). In other words, irony should be considered a very particular and recognizable thing, as defined above, and thus, to refer to everything *odd, coincidental, eerie, absurd* or *strangely funny* as ironic is, frankly, an abomination upon the Lord. [Re that last clause: not irony, but a simple, wholesome, American-born *exaggeration*]. To illustrate the many more things that are not ironic but are often referred to as such, let's look at some sample sentences, starring a wee wayward pup known as Benji, and see if we can illuminate some distinctions.

> SAMPLE: *Benji was run over by a bus. Isn't that* ironic?
> NO: That is not *ironic*. That is *unfortunate*, but it is not *ironic*.

> SAMPLE: *It was a bright and sunny day when Benji was run over by a bus. Ironic, no?*
> AGAIN, NO: That is not *irony*. It is an instance of *dissonance* between weather and tragedy.

> SAMPLE: *It is ironic that Benji was on his way to the vet when he was run over by a bus.*
> STILL: That is not *irony*. That is a *coincidence* that might be called *eerie*.

> SAMPLE: *It is ironic that Benji was run over on the same day he misused the word* ironic.
> BUT SEE: This is, again, a coincidence. It is *wonderfully appropriate* that he was run over on this day, deserving as he was of punishment, but it is not *ironic*.

> SAMPLE: *Is it not ironic that on the side of the bus that ran over Benji was an advertisement for "The Late Show with David Letterman," a show which many consider often* ironic?
> OH, OH: No. No.

2. Now, on a related subject: simply because humor is found in a context of pain, does not make that *humor ironic*. I have heard people claim that there is irony in the first chapter of this book, a chapter that is excruciatingly serious and straight-

forward. Are there even a few funny moments in this section? Absolutely not. But what confuses some people is the use of a device here or there, a formal trick or innovation that this sort of reader finds bothersome in the same way that a certain king of lore is to have told a certain court composer that his music had *too many notes*. And to this king or impatient reader I say: Yes, we should perhaps continue to write exactly as everyone has written before, though evermore plainly and clearly and simply, and yes perhaps we should refrain from any deviations from our copyright page/dedication/epigraph/sentence/sentence/paragraph/chapter/chapter/denouement structure, but then again, equally appealing might be, say, the injection of hot boiling acid, via titanium funnel, into our navels, while eating maggot-covered glass, while at lunch, in midtown Manhattan, at noon, in late July. 3. If we dismiss the idea that all *formal fun*—and we must be allowed it—constitutes *irony*, then we must agree that: 5. Prefaces are not ironic. 6. Notations are not ironic. 7. Diagrams are not ironic. 8. Funny titles are not ironic. 9. Numbered points are not ironic. 10. Footnotes are not ironic.[1] 11. Small type is not ironic. 11a. Even smaller type, used to illuminate more minor points and themes and aspects, is also without *irony*, and can be used just because the author feels fit to do so, as self-indulgent (not *ironic*) as it may seem, for example:

No, John ≠ Steve; No, w/r/t *Staggering Genius*: not as in some genius staggering around, but as in the final work being something of such genius that it would induce staggering, for its stupendousness. Of course the author never thought anyone would mentally apply to article A before *Genius* (by those imagining that that was the meaning meant), b/c he did not think book was actually anything much of this G-word at all, and so thought titling it this way would be funny, and would bring out objections from the humorless, which would also be funny. There was a practice, in the author's household, of mock-serious supra-self-congratulation, as hinted at in one of the earlier chapters w/r/t my father. It was not enough for him to be a good lawyer, he had to be The Greatest Ever Lawyer of Chicago. Thus, we inherited his taste for hyperbole, thus we find such hyperbole funny, thus we like to express ourselves with the use of such hyperbole, thus we are duly amused when certain among the tightly sphinctered cannot abide such hyperbole and get their claws in a bunch about it all; Yes these were almost used in front matter, possible subheads, where This Was Uncalled For sits: A wretched work of desperation; A homely book, grasping and drowning; An unshapely work of hatred and guilt; A clumsy thing — no modesty, little hope; A work at once very small and hugely annoying; A tedium of ugliness and pathos; a book of unwitting sadness; Yes but self-awareness *is* sincerity (lack of self-awareness is either ridiculous (is it possible to be *un*aware of one's... *self*?) or feigned, and feigned lack of self-awareness is lying, which is insincere, yes?; Yes I meant to show you all a draft, and so softest apologies to Ken/Ann/Stup/Les/Roger/Diedre/Jim/D-B/Matt; Yes, the quote in that one part was from Abbie Hoffman; No, John ≠ Dan (tho Legos=Dan (brtwd)); Yes everything was predicted, everything came to pass, everything is there, as in Bible—check Namibia, check cannibalism, check self-ob = boring, check treatment of/perception of A. Rich & others in pblc eye + apply lbrlly here—all there, all painfully foreseen: semi-celebration/cheering on gives *way* to suspicion b/c others' enthusiasm *g.u:t* self-loathing transferred from mirror to he like you/*g.u:t* to impatience/*g.u:t bklsh*; Yes Provoke the Petulant; Yes Anger the Small; Yes Make the Constipated Ever-More Cross-Eyed and Pained; Yes Place a Target on Your Heart and Hope for Release; Yes Freedom is being too tired to fight; Tell us: who will be left standing, NYW's? Who will do, and who will pooh-pooh?; Yes M.5¢. called it shame, shame of the performer, shame of standing and doing and projecting, the need to do so unsquelchable and yet horrible and flamboyant, and so compensated with plane-flying, horse-riding, boot-wearing, excessive swearing and swaggering; No John ≠ DK; Z=Ythfl optmsm/enn; P=Prvlg/nblss oblg; S=lte tkn/sddn/prblty o dth anytm/ SF=Bty/pssblry/absdy/new; Hills=hills; Frntr=wt o pst/fmt; Dncg= nly whn yng; Ocn=Yes, Kingwell; ≠ Xtian; Because we are the same, that's why spks Δ, why childhood pnrd; Some details borrowed from some wrongly; Frsbee = psh/pll btw sblngs/fmly/prnts/chldrn, also = release/ptntl; Man in elevator, going down = Benji = NYW's = Yeats' Eunuchs = prt insp fr frnt mttr; Ki & Mi now married, in SF; Yes, for yng to be jdgd by the un-yng = fruitless/unseemly/pathetic for the latter &/but jetfuel for the former; No, dog no longer with us, named Whisky, dead eight years now, owned by Marny, mourned, here immortalized via photoshop; No, Mentn of Big Country not kidding at all (plse find *The Crossing, unparalled!*); Yes but this section was at one point 68 pp; Yes like an infantryman who thought he was prepared but was not, wklg thru jungle, not knowing where next shot would come from, which sniper; Uly? Hadn't finished it, point/argument moot; BdM so sad, frail and departing *on* resentment, a waste; Yes W-W:100; Hspc: 200; FrshAr: 100; Lg: 20; Grn: 50; Y:10; Msc: 50; Among the trunk-art-takers and their purported hobbies: Hansi Linn/drinking a lot of gin; Matt Fisher/eating beans; Peter Curran/stalking Debbie Gibson; Billy Allen/biking; Doug McDermott/mice; Eddie Lamiere/spelunking; Danielle McArthur & Michael Murray/being sensitive; Ryan Schroeder/building stuff/drawing/kissing; Mark Pabst/berating the psuedo-hipness of my socioeconomic class; Scott Bowers/wandering around; Douglas Jones/ice fishing; Tim Rossi/heckling people watching film noir; dream involved white underwear; Yes, gone from NY, tired of worrying about one of us, or anyone, getting pushed in front of a train. In that city, literally and literarily, it happens every day.

Now, further: 11. Appendices are not ironic. 12. Having characters break out of character is not ironic. Wait, back to humor for a second: Generally, if a joke *is* told, or a humorous anecdote relayed, and by chance you do not understand that joke or humorous anecdote, it does not mean it is *ironic*. Or *"neo-ironic."* It simply means that you do not understand that joke. And that is okay. When you do not understand a joke, or do not want to read something in very small type, it is not necessary to become angry. You may simply move on, confidently, or, if you choose, you may take a 'book break,' by putting it down, and then enjoying a nice walk through your garden, or sitting by a window with a nice cool Bartles & Jaymes sixer. Still, we have reached a point, with a certain group of venally impatient and yet startlingly lazy cultural bystanders, wherein everything in the world falls into two categories: the Earnest and the Ironic. And neither, it seems, is acceptable. Everything is either glib and shallow, or maudlin and boring. This book, however, has been in a strange position: many many readers, in particular those close to its author and who have read too much and talked too much about having read too much, have felt that the book was too naked, too raw, and much too sentimental: in sum, too earnest. Many were these people, for example, who felt that the entire story should have been told within the structure of the front matter, therefore better couched/clothed. At the very same time, there were those who felt that the front matter was (and is) *pomo garbage*, and that as a result, the entire story is being told with a tongue in its author's cheek, a wink toward the skybox—these people saying, in essence, Good God, why couldn't he simply have left the story, as poignant as it is, be? So. This book cannot win. For some, at least. And when this book is not winning, attached to it are labels: *Post* this, *meta* that. Oh gosh. Where to start? These are the sorts of prefixes used by those without opinions. In place of saying simply 'I liked it' or 'I did not like it' they attempt to fence its impact by affixing to it these meaningless stickers. Oh, we should free ourselves from these terms, used only to make confusing something that we already understand. Because honestly: everyone who actually reads this book, or any book, will understand it. So I beg of you:

PEOPLE, FRIENDS, PLEASE: TRUST YOUR EYES, TRUST YOUR EARS, TRUST YOUR ART.

It is only when we skim, or hear something second-hand, or form an opinion before reading or viewing with open mind and heart, that we misunderstand and thus apply diminutive labels. See here: I do not live in a postmodern time. I did not live in a time when something *new* was called *modern*, so for me there is no such thing as *modern*, and thus there cannot be

---

[1] What the fuck is ironic about this?

anything *postmodern*. For me, where I am standing, it is all New. The world, every day, is New. Only for those born in, say, 1870 or so, can there be a meaningful use of the term postmodernism, because for the rest of us we are born and we see and from what we see and digest we remake our world. And to understand it we do not need to label it, categorize it. These labels are slothful and dismissive, and so contradict what we already know about the world, and our daily lives. We know that in each day, we laugh, and we are serious. We do *both*, in the *same* day, *every day*. But in our art, we expect clear distinction between the two. We expect a movie to be a *comedy* or a *drama*. We expect writing to be *serious writing* or *humorous writing*. But imagine if the same thing were done to describe one's hours or days: Every day, when we buy a lollipop at the corner store, we hear a joke; someone banters with us; at home we see something ha-ha in the newspaper; we watch something funny on TV; a friend tells a good story that makes us laugh. And all these things happen even on the days when other, horrible things happen. But we don't label our days Serious Days or Humorous Days. We know that each day contains endless nuances—if written would contain dozens of disparate passages, funny ones, sad ones, poignant ones, brutal ones, the terrifying and the cuddly. But we are often loathe to allow this in our art. And that is too bad, but can be corrected if we all join me and submit to this very reasonable proposal, one which I have long been working on, a proposal that was once 612 pages but will soon be submitted to our Congress and other of the world's legislative bodies and could very well be enacted here and everywhere because it has been whittled down to the simple plaintive plea:

KILL THE HUMORLESS.

Now, can ever *humorous writing* be considered *serious writing*? It can, but—and this is a very important point—for humorous writing to be serious writing, *it cannot actually be funny*. It can be witty. But it cannot be funny. Also, it cannot be too witty. After a certain amount of wit you become clever, and to be clever is necessarily to be *too clever for his or her own good*. Now to sum up: Serious, witty, and heartfelt = good. Funny, clever and earnest = not good. Irony, of course is very much ≠ good. All that said, all previous objections aside, there are a few ironic moments in this book (remember, way back when, I did say 'almost'). The ironic parts occur when the writings and themes of *Might* magazine are related. We find it, used sparingly and for a reason, in the passages describing the people behind and antics resulting from *Might* magazine, a periodical which often made its points by being sarcastic. For example, we might say "We very much like war," even though we actually meant *just the opposite*. When the book was first read and reviewed, a vast majority of these careful and openhearted readers saw the reason for the *Might* passages clearly, and well they should have, because it was made much too obvious: that *Might*, and its ironic contents, were included in the book simply so that they could be knocked down and picked apart. Again and again, the words spoken through *Might*, and its often sneering messages—which displace its purveyors' initially purple and Utopian hopes—are attacked in the narrative, and in the end, we see that *Might* dies. And at the same time that Skye dies, *Might* dies, and Skye's death humbles us all, makes us all feel like imbeciles for the time we've spent spitting acidic stomach juices (ah!) onto everything we see. We see that while we're having fun with a faked death of a child star, one of our own falls from a building and barely remains in this world. In the end, the events of actual life completely overwhelm the endless self-examination that *Might* represented, and the magazine dies, and its carcass is abandoned, and actual things take over, and obliterate our glibness, and finally give way to the long messy run-on of the book's end. Speaking of which, there have been a few readers who have taken even *that* passage as ironic. Which is so disturbing. A parody of *Ulysses*? What is wrong with you people? But such interpretations, in the end, aren't really my problem. When I was done, I was ashamed, because I had written what I saw as a much too revealing and maudlin thing, overflowing with blood and sentiment and a simple bare longing for people who are gone. The book was seen by its author as a stupid risk, and an ugly thing, and a betrayal, and overall, as a mistake he would regret for the rest of his life but a mistake which nevertheless he could not refrain from making, and worse, as a mistake he would encourage everyone to make, because everyone should make big, huge mistakes, because a) They don't want you to; b) Because they haven't the balls themselves and your doing it reminds them of their status as havers-of-no-balls; c) Because your life is worth documenting; d) Because if you do not believe your life is worth documenting, or knowing about, then why are you wasting your time/our time? Our air? e) Because if you do it right and go straight toward them you like me will write to them, and will looking straight into their eyes when writing, will look straight into their fucking eyes, like a person sometimes can do with another person, and tell them something because even though you might not know them well, or at all, and even if you wrote in their books or hugged them or put your hand on their arm, you still would scarcely know them, but even so wrote a book that was really a letter to them, a messy fucking letter that you could barely keep a grip on, but a letter you meant, and a letter you sometimes wish you had not mailed, but a letter you are happy that made it from you to them.

p. 294, paragraph 2: *Bloodstream*

This did not happen as stated. While writing the book, I had a dream that I was inside and streaming through not Toph's but my *sister*'s bloodstream. I changed and inserted this here because it seemed like a good idea at the time.

p. 348, paragraph 7: *Adam Rich*

I'm not sure if Adam said exactly those words. I'm not sure he talked precisely about a costume drama. I do know that he spoke of a period piece, but beyond that, I was filling in, taking small liberties. Which was patently unfair. I had no right to put words in his mouth, and I had no right to treat him the away I did, which was not all *that* bad, but there was in my portrait a trace of condescension, and I'm ashamed, now, of having done this to him. It was a strange thing: even while I was, in the book, basically denouncing our motives at the time we faked his death, I'm writing of him in a way that is less than fully respectful. So: I am not sure his project-in-progress was indeed a costume drama. The funny thing, of course, was that his on-air personality eerily mirrored that of his in-magazine one, wherein he was an auteur sitting on a secret and great project. In this interview, he alluded to the project he was working on. Now listen to this: while I was in L.A., shortly after the publication of the book, I was at a horrible bar somewhere, full of people in wide-lapel shirts, and who should walk by but that selfsame Adam Rich, with a few friends. He either saw me and decided not to say hi, or he did not see me. I saw him and decided not to say anything, for fear he might be sore, and have a weapon.

p. 361, paragraph 6: *Back to that house*
I have been back to my hometown once since the original publication of this book. I have been asked to come a few times, and have politely declined, thinking that if anywhere someone might emerge from a group to plug me with a bullet, it might be there, though I have no good reason, outside of strange and unreasonable premonitions, to believe this would be so. So when I did come back it was an accidental visit, unplanned and probably ill-advised, begun at 3 a.m. and lasting a mere twenty minutes or so. It was all wrong and perfect.

It started at a wedding. A friend from high school, let's call her Jane, was marrying another friend, let's call him Philippe de Beetenbottom. They were being married on a small island in southern Michigan, and I went with a friend to the wedding, which required flying into O'Hare and driving three hours, through Indiana and up into Michigan. The wedding happened, was very nice, and was populated, oddly enough, by precisely the same group of people who attended the Polly wedding described in the main text. And like at that wedding, there was the feeling of being overly grateful to be with all of these people, and of wanting to hold on to them too long, to dive into them somehow and stay under.

To make an early morning flight, my friend and I had to leave the reception at midnight to drive straight to O'Hare. We said goodbye just after the band had quit for the night, then drove down through Micheana and left through Indiana and then up through Chicago's South Side, up wide and clear Lake Shore Drive and then we were in Chicago's Loop and with a few hours to kill. My friend had never seen Lake Forest, so we decided to plow through the city and all the way up, to rummage around in the dark there for a while, then head back to O'Hare.

We snuck into town at about 3:10 a.m. and it was black-black, no stars, no moon. Because my old house stood near the town's southern limits, we went there first. We pulled off the highway, rolled quietly down Old Elm Road, and then onto my street, Waveland. With the trees overhanging and the night unlit, we saw almost nothing—a landscape covered in soot. Our headlights blew softly into the black, illuminating very little. A few bends of the road and we stopped in front of my house and then I was there and the car was stopped and as usual, I felt nothing. It looked good. It looked the same. It looked fine. How many times am I going to stop in front of that house and wait for something to happen? When will that house, under my gaze, through the windshield of this or that rental car, finally unmoor itself and fly away?

We left, drove up Green Bay Road, which runs straight through the town, and along which stand the old huge houses. It felt good to be here so late. It was safe to drive through, to stay in the car and slide through undetected. No one would see us, no one would say anything. We were happily motoring along, the radio indulging some '80s station, when we passed an ancient, very pretty ivy-drenched mansion. We slowed down, stopped, looking down the driveway. The estate shrugged smugly.

Then, from about a quarter mile up, pulling out of the Onwentsia Country Club, headlights. They came toward us. With a queer idea that it might be an officer of the law, I made our car move, heading toward the town's business district, hoping to slip past him unmolested. When we were about to pass him, the headlights became clearly a police car, a searchlight flashed wildly toward us, imploring. We stopped.

Many of you know that in small and uneventful hamlets, the police have a very few tasks, those being: 1) to make sure no inappropriate-looking people enter the town's borders (usually driving inappropriate-looking cars) and 2) to make it virtually impossible for teenagers to live happy teenaged lives. Thus, we spent a lot of time, in high school, being pulled over by these vigilant officers, and worrying while they plundered our cars with their flashlights.

In the middle of the road, going opposite directions, he rolled down his window, and I did the same. His mustache was Ditka's.

"What's up?" he said. Also, Ditka hair.

I explained that we were doing some sightseeing, that I had grown up here, and was showing my friend around.

He stared at me.

"What was your address?" he asked.

I told him.

More staring. Then he let us go.

We drove on, but a quick check into the rearview mirror confirmed a guess: that he would turn around and follow us. We drove another half mile and turned at St. Mary's, my old church. We stopped before the entrance. There was a banner draped left to right over the old red brick facade, noting the church's 150th birthday. It did not look like the front door was open. It had always been open at odd times.

Then we felt his presence. He had pulled his car even with ours. His window was open. I rolled mine down.

"So what is it now?" he said.

I explained that I was looking at my church. It occurred to me that this was my first cop-car encounter since the midnight beach, the wallet and the kids in Los Angeles. I looked at Ditka. I wondered if he knew me. I wondered if he knew me as the boy who grew up vandalizing this town, breaking its windows, aiming wristrockets at its streetlamps, eggs at its walls, rocks at its police cars, defacing its playgrounds, lighting its streets on fire. He could know me, could know that my friends and I lived to cause havoc here, to make things less pretty, to make green things brown and white things grey. And if he knew about this book...

"Listen, you already stopped us once. I told you what we were doing. Now you're hassling us in front of my church. I spent twenty years in this town. Doesn't that grant me the right to come back and look around?"

"Well," he said, "we've had some robberies lately, and when I see a car stopping in front of different buildings, I take notice."

There had been no more than four crimes committed in the last half-century in this town, and yet again and again these robberies were cited, to provide entree to the cars of anyone unusual passing through. We stared at each other for a long time. I knew things about this town he never could. I wanted my rental car to morph into a monster truck, and in this monster truck I would drive over this police car, I would reduce it to foil.

"So what do we do now?" I said.

He shrugged extravagantly. "Nothing," he said.

"Okay," I said. I was being tough.

"Okay," he said, squinting.

"Okay," I said. Tougher yet: "Bye."

And he rolled away.

The church was closed. We drove to the beach and it was closed. We drove to the high school, pristine, abandoned, lit like a monument, closed. We went back through the town square and down Deerpath, leaving. On our way out of town, we passed the police station, where two squad cars, occupied, were parked, facing the road, and as we went by, their headlights made ghosts of us, and I wondered if they knew who I was and what I had done.

p. 379, paragraph 13: *Funeral home names of coffins*
I made up the names of these coffins.

p. 418, paragraph 3: *Skye died*
We were not all in the room when we received news of Skye's passing.

p. 425, paragraph 17: *Shalini now*
I completely guessed about the coma being two weeks long, fully expecting to be corrected. But it turns out I was right, and was not all that far off about most of the events. Now, because people often ask how Shalini's doing these days, and because there is much to tell, we'll let her explain. Shal wrote this for you, in early October, 2000.

"I have a headache right now, but that's not unusual. Since my accident happened, I've had them a lot.

The accident occurred on February 17, 1996. I was at a farewell party for a friend, and fourteen of us fell four floors to the concrete below, when a wooden balcony came away from the side of the building. Three of us were pinned under the balcony, where I suffered a crushed skull. My family was told not to rush to the hospital because I had less than a 5 percent chance to survive.

I was in a coma for two weeks and I was in the hospital for eight months. During my hospitalization I underwent innumerable brain surgeries, including a V.P. shunt, which involves installing tubing that runs from my brain into my scalp, under the skin of my neck, chest, and ends in my belly inside my abdomen. I need this to survive. The most crucial surgery was the reconstruction of my skull bones. At the time of the accident, it became necessary to remove a major bony skull on the right and left side, because my brain was swelling like a balloon and had no place to expand.

Eventually, they had to replace my cranium. I received a synthetic porous artificial skull, and a few days after replacement, my physical condition started to improve. My shaking and trembling stopped, but I was still unable to walk, sit, or talk. I didn't know what I was doing. During my hospital stay, I also suffered a stroke, which affected my right side. After I stabilized physically, the nursing and physical therapy staff at Mount Zion Hospital in San Francisco taught me how to sit, stand, scoot in bed, regain my balance and eventually walk and talk.

I was constantly in a dreamlike state, not understanding anything that happened or what I was going through, or what the end result would be. I was determined, however, to live. In the end of August of 1996, I was released from the hospital and sent home to Southern California, where I still live with my family. (The events I'm describing to you are not only vague, they're absent from my memory—I don't really remember what happened to me before, during or after my accident. Most of this information has been related to me by my mother and family members.)

For my brain rehabilitation, I enrolled in the "Acquired Brain Injury Program" at Coastline Community College in Costa Mesa, California. I never liked the name of that college—"Acquired Brain Injury"—it's too much of a euphemism, reminding me of the acquisition of stocks and bonds. But I made it through, and eventually won the contest to give the graduation speech for my class. I wrote it and with great difficulty even *memorized* it—not easy for me!

Now I'm writing again, mostly books for children with dyslexia. The two women for whom I work, at the National Dyslexia Research Foundation (N.D.R.F.) are understanding, and help me with my rehabilitation as well. They help my brain functions by playing strategic card games with me. Speaking of cards, there's a 79-year-old woman who comes to my house, three times a week, to help me improve my reading speed. Since I have visual defects in both of my eyes, we practice reading using large fonts in childrens' books. She's full of energy for a woman her age!

But there's only one problem; actually, two or three problems: Having been a very social person for most of my life, it's difficult to accept the fact that my friends have moved out and on with their lives. (I get attached easily.) College friends have gotten married, had kids, own pets and even their own cars. (I have to be seizure-free for two years before I can drive again.) Two of my friends asked me to be a bridesmaid in their nuptials in October. And it sucks because they're getting married on the same day, but in different states—one on the West coast and the other in the East! Decisions, decisions. Either way, I'm excited to see my friends. I've seen them since my accident—it seems like forever-and-a-day—but I don't remember exactly what we did.

Since 1997 I have relearned how to ski, swim, dance and all my social skills have returned. I would like so much to be independent again. My goals, therefore, are to continue to improve my brain's thought processes. I also want to try to read more fluidly. I want to reach my goal of being independent again, driving myself and others around (the carpool lane has its advantages), and basically be without "adult supervision" (I'll be 30 next month!). I don't know what my professional capabilities are yet, but I'll keep trying, whether it's publishing again, or being a professional music or video D.J. (Did I mention I'm taking singing lessons?)"

This appendix was written, in part, in L.A., about an hour from Shalini's home. I saw her yesterday, and she looked perfect, all of her perfect. We sat on the carpet, watching the first Gore/Bush presidential debate while talking about arranged marriages with her grandmother (hers was wildly successful: "Oh, when I saw him he was sooo handsome!"). Then we went with her mom and stepfather to see the new house they're building, on the site of their old house. We walked through at dusk, the sun setting through the wall of windows at the house's rear. We stepped slowly through the darkening rooms, Shalini holding tight to my forearm, cautious with her feet, navigating the dusty wires and bricks. We walked up the curved central staircase to her new room, still being painted, high-ceilinged and empty of furniture. Through the windows Shalini was trying to point out Catalina Island, but we weren't sure if the lights we were seeing were it, or a boat, or some other island. We were in almost the exact place we had been four years before, at her party. We were at the same height, with the same view of the Pacific, but of course everything was different. We were now in an entirely new house, built atop the foundation of the other, though this one was grander, with even more sweeping views of the sea. And with everything painted white and all the rooms empty, it had a cool, ethereal feel to it.

I mentioned this to her, how her new house seemed like a house, in heaven, at dusk. I could barely see her, but she indulged me.

"Yeah, maybe," her silhouette said, with a chuckle.

p. 428, paragraph 8: *We're moving*
And so we are again, an escape from cold (too often in both senses) NY. While repacking old soft boxes full of trouble, I came into a haphazardly packed box and in it found a letter from my mom, which must have been written a year or so before everything got hairy. I was stunned by how many echoes I heard, stunned by how clearly and deftly much of this book, its themes and even its punctuation, is hinted at in her short note. It is reprinted below for this reason, and because it is a nice note and you will like it and hear a voice that should immediately sound familiar and good.

Dear Bill, Beth & Dave,

Sorry to put you through all the recent anxiety that you all feel—keep a positive attitude and together, as we have with many things in the past, we will beat this too. It's just one of the many bad breaks that life holds and getting through them makes us all that much stronger.

I'm back at work and having a great time with all my little friends. The staff at school have been very helpful in all respects so all goes well. I've heard from a great many people (out of the woodwork, so to speak), all offer their help. They call almost daily and check on me or offer more information about possible treatment.

I go to see another surgeon Friday afternoon in Evanston andone at the University of Chicago Hospital Tuesday for more opinions—the consensus so far is for more surgery for the best chance to get this pesky type of cancer—so will let you know when I'm going in again—this would be my idea of the best way to go.

Enough of this—all is fine—all is well—don't worry—

Chris is fine—can read pretty well now—he reads the books each night instead of me—he is still in soccer but as usual his team is not aggressive—wait for the ball to come—kick it—watch it go and sort of smile at it—never go after it tho—one more game—next year he should get more coaching and training for position. He starts a cartooning class at Gorton [Community Center] tomorrow so "he can draw like David" and woodworking another day. I asked him to join a pre-Cub Scout group and he said and I quote "I wouldn't be humiliated by wearing that outfit to school." He uses this word a lot lately—did he get it from one of you?

Am watching horrifying news program of an earthquake in San Francisco—that state is going into the ocean so Bill and Beth get out of there—no place to settle. Tried to get Beth since Berkeley is supposed to be hit bad but cannot get through—

Dad is fine and a wonderful support at this time—

For Halloween, Chris will be a bird—that was his choice—a "King Bird"—we got a headdress and will improvise from there—hopefully, I'll be home to see him but if not, Patty G. will see that he has a good time, or his favorite, Mrs. B.

Chris has new friends at school—they are great together—he is having such a good year—except for gym—got his report from Mr. O'Neill (remember your reports?) and apparently he cannot do pull-ups or situps but is way up there in the running races—he will need improvement (says Mr. O'Neill) so we'll all have to work on it when you get home—ha ha!

Well all for today—

Love you all—

Mom

People tell me stories of death. I am the person to tell about the deaths they have watched, the people who left them too soon. And when I meet the people who have seen people go, as I'm drawing some stupid picture in their book—usually some variation on wood planks, or tree trunks, or ears—they say that they are sure that by now I've probably heard "enough sad stories from crazy people at readings." A woman recently said this to me, as she crouched at the table in front of me, in Denver, and when she added, "You're nice enough just to come here," it occurred to me, in an enlightened moment, that she was being dumb. I was in Denver because I had received a request, through the mail, from a young woman named Amy Slothower, who works in a volunteer capacity for the Webb-Waring Institute for Cancer, Aging, and Antioxidant Research. She wanted to know if I would come out and speak at a fund-raising dinner. I got the letter on a Sunday, and left her a message right then, knowing she wouldn't get it until the following day. I couldn't wait, because, frankly, I was really goddamned excited. I had never been asked to help raise funds before, not in any significant way, with the exception of solicitations from the gentlemen down on Fourth Ave., Brooklyn, always trying to scrape together money for a bus ticket to Atlantic City. So, Denver: I was supposed to leave Friday, to spend a weekend in Colorado before the fund-raiser on Tuesday. But in an instance of not *irony* but perhaps *perverse appropriateness*, two days before leaving for the cancer fund-raiser I was served a summons, at a public reading—I was being sued by a former agent for money generated from my family's story. I flew to Denver in a fog of legal worry, but it was all soon obliterated by meeting Ms. Slothower with her fragile eyes, and even more so when we visited the institute and were given a tour of the facilities. I met the researchers there, all of whom, inexplicably, put down their basically life-saving work to talk to me, stabbing at questions—*So, why don't the cells just fix themselves?* or *That loud beeping sound, is that good or bad?*—while wearing a stained skateboard T-shirt, pilfered from Toph. We talked to about ten different scientists, each of whom was attacking a variation of the same problem. After introductions, each would start excitedly, some with Adam West's rhythm, explaining what they were working on, how tantalizingly close they were to this or that solution or breakthrough re breast cancer, diabetes, emphysema—*"If we... just ... figure... out WHY the... mutated cells don't kill themselves..."*—and the hunger to fix and cure was immediately contagious: within minutes I felt like I'd wasted decades; I wanted to drop everything, to move to Denver and become their Igor, sleeping on a basement cot.

Later I talked with the head of the institute, John Repine, about how woefully underfunded medical research, as opposed to treatment, was in this country, and he used a term that I don't think I'd heard before: he called what were doing, and what they sought funding for, as "blue sky research." Those words together sounded very good. He's talking about trying something that seems to most completely stupid, something with only a tenuous grip on logic, something that of course has never been tried before, involving great risk, and the willingness, at all times, to be completely wrong, and to look like an idiot. Three more words that sound good: Hot wet napkin.

When my parents passed on, and we read their wills, we discovered something we didn't at all expect, especially from our devoutly Catholic mother: they had both left instructions that their bodies be donated to science. We were bewildered and we were pissed. They wanted their cadavers to be used by medical students, they wanted their flesh to be cut into and their cancerous organs examined. We were breathless. They wanted no elaborate funerals, no expense incurred for such stuff—they hated wasting money or time on ceremony, on appearances. When they died there was little left—the house, the cars. And their bodies, and they gave those away. To offer them to strangers was disgusting, wrong, embarrassing. And selfish to us, their children, who would have to live with the thought of their cold weight sinking on silver tables, surrounded by students chewing gum and making jokes about the location of freckles. But then again: Nothing can be preserved. It's all on the way out, from the second it appears, and whatever you have always has one eye on the exit, and so screw it. As hideous and uncouth as it is, we have to give it all away, our bodies, our secrets, our money, everything we know: All must be given away, given away every day, because to be human means:

1. To be good
2. To save nothing

So when Amy first wrote to me—a long beautiful letter, I should say—I was daunted and thrilled. Eventually I gave them a meandering and infrequently coherent little speech, saved only by Tim Collins, a board member who at one point took the podium to sing his version of Led Zeppelin's "Whole Lotta Love." (Long story.) And I promised that when the lawsuits were done, I'd give the institute a wad of the kind of silly money that's come to me and my family via this book, money that was never mine and could never be mine. I wanted to throw it somewhere, I wanted that money gone. I wanted to be a part of what these people were doing, what others like them are doing, what my parents wanted to be a part of, to throw themselves into the flood to try and stop it, to feel the rush of feeling useful, feeling the justification of one's flesh. When do we feel this? War, mountain-climbing, sex—what? Yes our

bodies feel at home in war but why? Our bodies love to be soaked in sex
but why? Our bodies love to run in the rain—I subconsciously put off
returning movies just so I can run down the street, when it's pouring,
before the store closes, *to feel urgency*—because this part of us craves pur-
pose. *Give me something to do!* it yells. *For Christ's sake, tell me what to fucking do!* And when you know, when you've been given this, Oh, you feel
at peace. It feels so good, and you do not ever want to go back. Ask a
teacher, ask an ambulance driver. When my parents were sick, I began,
during my senior year in college, to drive back and forth from school to
home, usually from Thursday (I had only one, completely skippable,
class on Friday) to Sunday night, when I'd head back down state. The
drive between Champaign and Chicago is impossibly uneventful, completely tedious, and I was doing it, for the most part, in a 1981 Rabbit
without a radio or windshield wipers. But I did it with a certain smugness, with a sense of mission, because I was leaving the frivolity of college and my many housemates and their endless games of 9-ball (on the
pool table, my father's, that I had brought with me that fall, because he
wasn't playing much anymore). I was leaving that environment for a
place where, I felt, I was needed urgently, where I could lift sandbags,
put my finger in the dike, whatever. We all know that there are very few
times when we feel like we are proving we are using this flesh-life-
thing, and those times are during: a) sex; b) adventure; c) adventure in
the service of duty. And coming with that certain smugness was of
course a certain guilt about smugness drawn from duty. We feel glad
that we have a very tangible reason to exist, that we are driving on a terrible flat highway for three hours Thursday night because at home our
sister will say Finally! and our small brother will jump and monkey-hug
and say Hey stupid! and our parents will greet us with their exhaustion
and frail arms. And one night, that fall, thinking of coming home to
this we will be driving a new car, because the Rabbit will give out one
day, and will be replaced with a 1978 Chevrolet station wagon, brown.
And upon purchasing the car, there will be a light on in the car, a red
light urging the checking of the engine, a light ignored because the car
has just been cleared by a certified and unbiased mechanic. And after the
car has been owned and driven for no more than three weeks, it will be
in the process of making its way home, one late Thursday night through
the right side of the Illinois upper, and it will finally give out, about ten
miles from home, on Highway 41, the main commuter highway from

Chicago to the north suburbs. It will be raining heavily, and it will be cold, Lake Michigan October cold, and the rain will be coming at an angle. It will be about 11 o'clock, and the roads will be empty. When the car expires we will immediately know that the car is gone-gone, and we will leave it there on the highway, take from it our backpack, and we will put our arms through both straps, and start walking. We will know it's a few miles to the nearest gas station, either way, so we'll be determined to find a house, closer, and use their phone to call home to plead for rescue. But there will be a wall hugging the highway, and though there is a subdivision on the wall's other side, there will be, seemingly, no way to scale this wall. The wall will seem to have no end. We will be soaked. We will be cold. Our backpack, containing clothes and homework, will be shiny with rain. Finally we will climb a tree, near the wall, and we will get close enough to the wall to jump from the tree onto the wall, very much hurting our torso, and we will then harrumph up and straddle the fence, and then will jump from it to the grass below, which is wet, muddy and upon which we will fall, completely, to our knees. We will wonder if this is a good thing or a bad thing that something like this should be happening three weeks after purchasing this car, while on the way home to watch the fetid air and breathe the dowel-legs and walk up from the basement and ready our eyes for anything. We will get up from the brown smooth ground and will walk toward the lights and pick a house in the quiet neighborhood and descend on it like an ax-wielding person in a horror movie. We will feel terrible about ringing someone's bell at 11:30 on a Thursday, and for being so wet and tired. The people opening the door will be timid at first, scared, bug-eyed, an older couple with a warm safe home that does not receive visitors at that hour. They will listen and will let us in. They will feed and clothe us, and put our wet clothes in the dryer. The walls will be solid, painted peach. When talking, they and we will soon realize that they are the grandparents of a boy we've known since we were nine, who was on our soccer team. He was a goalie, a good one. Then hot chocolate and butter cookies. Then we will call home.

Our sister will answer.

We will say:

"Can I talk to Mom?"

She will say:

"She's asleep."

We will say:

"Oh. What about Dad?"

"Asleep."

"Well, I need a ride."

"Where are you?"

"My car died."

"The one you just bought?"

"Yeah. Listen, I'm at someone's house."

"Whose?"

"It doesn't matter. I need a ride."

"I can't leave. She's asleep, and Toph's here."

We will be without other options, and will beg our sister to do something, to please put Toph in the car, as late as it is, and come to pick us up, because if she cannot come these people will wonder about our family and why it is that a car cannot be dispatched to pick up a wet member not fifteen minutes away, sitting in borrowed slippers and shouldered by a blue wool blanket. The sister will agree and will hang up the phone. There will be some talking with the grandparents, who we will want to become our grandparents, who we will suspect might already know everything and are sad for us. Then there will be our clothes, fresh from the dryer, and we will change into them in the downstairs bathroom, which will be a pale yellow. Soon our mother's headlights will turn into the goalie's grandparents' driveway, and we will see our sister and young brother's faces in the car, under the lawn light, the windshield wet with diamonds. Our brother will be past his bedtime and duly wired. They will come to the door and we will introduce them to the grandparents, who will by now know everything, will have deduced that we are That Family, but before they can pity and question we will say thanks and jump from their porch and down their steps and through the rain to the car. We will sit in the passenger seat while driving home, will reach back to grab the boy's squishy stomach and he will pinch our hand and then drool on it, cackling, and we will be thinking of California and the sun there while heading home to the house of early sleeping.

p. 435, paragraph 2: 7 feet, 8 feet tall

And I was right. At 6'3" and rising, he is the tallest man our family line has yet produced. Do not mess with him. I mean that, good people.